PREFACE

In the 1980s and 1990s, the FBA published two keys for identifying larval Trichoptera found in Britain and Ireland. The first, published in 1981, was by J. M. Edington and A. G. Hildrew. This dealt with the caseless caddis larvae, describing 47 species, together with information on feeding, habitat and life histories. The key was immediately successful and a new edition was published in 1995. The much larger key to 125 species of case-bearing caddis larvae, by I. D. Wallace, B. Wallace and G. N. Philipson, was published in 1990. Again the key was much in demand and has been out of print for some time. The original authors, led by Ian Wallace, have re-examined the key and added to it in terms of subsequent information on distribution and different instars, and have made this new, updated edition much more user-friendly. Since 1990 a considerable amount of work has been carried out on the taxonomy and systematics of the families of case-bearing caddis: the text, illustrations and references reflect this additional information. This new edition incorporates improvements at several points in the text where some users of the 1990 edition have experienced confusion or difficulties, and also incorporates new couplets and text-figures to help improve identification of several species. Additional notes on the key couplets are provided and substantial improvements have been made in several parts of the key, particularly in the section on Limnephilidae, where some drawings are reproduced in several places to provide users with more convenient illustrations close to the appropriate key couplets.

The addition of 30 pages to the revised set of keys will, we believe, help in providing better discernment, illustration and description of the species presented in this volume. Meticulous attention to detail by such experienced authors, together with the experience of the FBA's editor, David Sutcliffe, will, I believe, provide a much improved, long awaited revision to this key. The Environment Agency has been most supportive in the publication of this key.

The Ferry House
March 2003

Roger Sweeting
Chief Executive, FBA

D1359808

CONTENTS

KEYS TO THE

CASE–BEARING CADDIS LARVAE OF BRITAIN AND IRELAND

by

I. D. WALLACE*
B. WALLACE
and
the late G. N. PHILIPSON

FRESHWATER BIOLOGICAL ASSOCIATION
SCIENTIFIC PUBLICATION No. 61

2003

Editor: D. W. SUTCLIFFE

* Address for correspondence:
Department of Zoology, Liverpool Museum, William Brown Street, Liverpool, L3 8EN, UK

Published by the Freshwater Biological Association, The Ferry House,
Far Sawrey, Ambleside, Cumbria LA22 0LP, UK

in association with

National Museums and Galleries on Merseyside

ISBN 0–900386–70–3

ISSN 0367–1887

INTRODUCTION

A 'caddis' is popularly considered to be an aquatic insect living in a portable tube or case which it has made from various materials. There are, however, many caddisflies whose larvae do not make cases and this difference in habit has resulted in a convenient division of Trichoptera larvae into 'case-bearing' and 'caseless'. Unfortunately, the division is not as precise as one might have hoped. Some 'case-bearing' larvae are caseless until they reach the final instar (Hydroptilidae); others may abandon their cases under certain circumstances and drift without cases in the stream flow (Glossosomatidae); a few, at least in captivity, readily leave and re-enter their cases (Phryganeidae). Conversely, 'caseless' larvae construct fixed shelters of various materials in which they live or pupate; such shelters, dislodged when sampling, may well be found to contain a larva which the unwary might consider to be 'case-bearing'. For such reasons, the families grouped as 'cased' or 'caseless' must be carefully defined on grounds of larval morphology.

It should also be borne in mind that the division of caddis into two groups depending on the presence or absence of a case during the development of the larva is not supported by their phylogeny. The division separates the Glossosomatidae and Hydroptilidae from the closely related caseless Rhyacophilidae.

CHECKLIST OF CASE–BEARING CADDIS
IN BRITAIN AND IRELAND

This checklist is taken from Barnard (1985). Redundant names used by Kimmins (1966) and Macan (1973) are shown in parentheses. Asterisks against species names indicate there are no authenticated records from Ireland (Ashe *et al.* 1998). *Apatania auricula* and *Limnephilus fuscinervis* have been recorded from Ireland but not from Britain.

Family	Genus	Species
GLOSSOSOMATIDAE	GLOSSOSOMA Curtis, 1834	*boltoni* Curtis, 1834
		conformis Neboiss, 1963
		* *intermedium* (Klapálek, 1892)
	AGAPETUS Curtis, 1834	*delicatulus* McLachlan, 1884
		fuscipes Curtis, 1834
		ochripes Curtis, 1834
HYDROPTILIDAE	AGRAYLEA Curtis, 1834	*multipunctata* Curtis, 1834
		sexmaculata Curtis, 1834
	ALLOTRICHIA McLachlan, 1880	*pallicornis* (Eaton, 1873)
	HYDROPTILA Dalman, 1819	*angulata* Mosely, 1922
		cornuta Mosely, 1922
		forcipata (Eaton, 1873)
		* *lotensis* Mosely, 1930
		martini Marshall, 1977
		occulta (Eaton, 1873)
		pulchricornis Pictet, 1834
		simulans Mosely, 1920
		sparsa Curtis, 1834
		* *sylvestris* Morton, 1898
		tigurina Ris, 1894
		tineoides Dalman, 1819
		* *valesiaca* Schmid, 1947
		* *vectis* Curtis, 1834
	OXYETHIRA Eaton, 1873	* *distinctella* McLachlan, 1880
		falcata Morton, 1893
		flavicornis (Pictet, 1834)
		frici Klapálek, 1891
		* *mirabilis* Morton, 1904
		sagittifera Ris, 1897
		simplex Ris, 1897
		tristella Klapálek, 1895
	TRICHOLEIOCHITON Kloet & Hincks, 1944	*fagesii* (Guinard, 1879)
	ITHYTRICHIA Eaton, 1873	*clavata* Morton, 1905
		lamellaris Eaton, 1873

	ORTHOTRICHIA Eaton, 1873	*angustella* (McLachlan, 1865) *costalis* (Curtis, 1834) * *tragetti* Mosely, 1930
PHRYGANEIDAE	AGRYPNETES McLachlan, 1876	* *crassicornis* (McLachlan, 1876)[1]
	AGRYPNIA Curtis, 1835	*obsoleta* (Hagen, 1864) (*Phryganea obsoleta*) *pagetana* Curtis, 1835 * *picta* Kolenati, 1848 *varia* (Fabricius, 1793) (*P. varia*)
	HAGENELLA Martynov, 1924	* *clathrata* (Kolenati, 1848) (*Oligotricha clathrata*)
	OLIGOTRICHA Rambur, 1842	*striata* (Linnaeus, 1758) (*O. ruficrus*)
	PHRYGANEA Linnaeus, 1758	*bipunctata* Retzius, 1783 (*P. striata*) *grandis* Linnaeus, 1758
	TRICHOSTEGIA Kolenati, 1848	* *minor* (Curtis, 1834)
BRACHYCENTRIDAE	BRACHYCENTRUS Curtis, 1834	* *subnubilus* Curtis, 1834
LEPIDOSTOMATIDAE	CRUNOECIA McLachlan, 1876	*irrorata* (Curtis, 1834)
	LASIOCEPHALA Costa, 1857	*basalis* (Kolenati, 1848)
	LEPIDOSTOMA Rambur, 1842	*hirtum* (Fabricius, 1775)
LIMNEPHILIDAE	IRONOQUIA Banks, 1916	* *dubia* (Stephens, 1837)
	APATANIA Kolenati, 1848	*auricula* (Forsslund, 1930) *muliebris* McLachlan, 1866 (*nielseni* Schmid, 1954)[2] *wallengreni* McLachlan, 1871
	DRUSUS Stephens, 1837	*annulatus* (Stephens, 1837)
	ECCLISOPTERYX Kolenati, 1848	*guttulata* (Pictet, 1834)
	ALLOGAMUS Schmid, 1955	* *auricollis* (Pictet, 1834)
	ENOICYLA Rambur, 1842	* *pusilla* (Burmeister, 1839)
	HALESUS Stephens, 1836	*digitatus* (Schrank, 1781) *radiatus* (Curtis, 1834)
	HYDATOPHYLAX Wallengren, 1891	*infumatus* (McLachlan, 1865)
	MELAMPOPHYLAX Schmid, 1955	* *mucoreus* (Hagen, 1861)
	MESOPHYLAX McLachlan, 1882	* *aspersus* (Rambur, 1842) *impunctatus* McLachlan, 1884
	MICROPTERNA Stein, 1874 (STENOPHYLAX)	*lateralis* (Stephens, 1837) *sequax* McLachlan, 1875

[1] The genus *Agrypnetes* was reinstated by Wiggins (1998).
[2] *A. nielseni* is now considered to be a form of *A. muliebris* (Barnard & O'Connor 1987).

LIMNEPHILIDAE POTAMOPHYLAX   *cingulatus* (Stephens, 1837)
               Wallengren, 1891   *latipennis* (Curtis, 1834)
                                            * *rotundipennis* (Brauer, 1857)

               STENOPHYLAX Kolenati, 1848   *permistus* McLachlan, 1895
                                            * *vibex* (Curtis, 1834)

               CHAETOPTERYX Stephens, 1829 *villosa* (Fabricius, 1798)

               ANABOLIA Stephens, 1837   *nervosa* (Curtis, 1834)

               GLYPHOTAELIUS Stephens, 1837 *pellucidus* (Retzius, 1783)

               GRAMMOTAULIUS Kolenati, 1848 *nigropunctatus* (Retzius, 1783)
                                            (*G. atomarius*)
                                            * *nitidus* (Müller, 1764)

               LIMNEPHILUS Leach, 1815   *affinis* Curtis, 1834
                                            auricula Curtis, 1834
                                            binotatus Curtis, 1834
                                            * *bipunctatus* Curtis, 1834
                                            * *borealis* (Zetterstedt, 1840)
                                            centralis Curtis, 1834
                                            coenosus Curtis, 1834
                                            decipiens (Kolenati, 1848)
                                            elegans Curtis, 1834
                                            * *extricatus* McLachlan, 1865
                                            flavicornis (Fabricius, 1787)
                                            * *fuscicornis* (Rambur, 1842)
                                            fuscinervis (Zetterstedt, 1840)
                                            griseus (Linnaeus, 1758)
                                            hirsutus (Pictet, 1834)
                                            ignavus McLachlan, 1865
                                            incisus Curtis, 1834
                                            lunatus Curtis, 1834
                                            luridus Curtis, 1834
                                            marmoratus Curtis, 1834
                                            nigriceps (Zetterstedt, 1840)
                                            pati O'Connor, 1980
                                            * *politus* McLachlan, 1865
                                            rhombicus (Linnaeus, 1758)
                                            sparsus Curtis, 1834
                                            stigma Curtis, 1834
                                            * *subcentralis* (Brauer, 1857)
                                            tauricus (Schmid, 1964)
                                            vittatus (Fabricius, 1798)

               NEMOTAULIUS Banks, 1906   * *punctatolineatus* (Retzius, 1783)

               PHACOPTERYX Kolenati, 1848   *brevipennis* (Curtis, 1834)
                                            (*Anabolia brevipennis*)

               RHADICOLEPTUS   * *alpestris* (Kolenati, 1848)
               Wallengren, 1891

GOERIDAE   GOERA Stephens, 1829   *pilosa* (Fabricius, 1775)

               SILO Curtis, 1833   *nigricornis* (Pictet, 1834)
                                            pallipes (Fabricius, 1781)

BERAEIDAE	BERAEA Stephens, 1833	*maurus* (Curtis, 1834)
		pullata (Curtis, 1834)
	BERAEODES Eaton, 1867	*minutus* (Linnaeus, 1761)
	ERNODES Wallengren, 1891	* *articularis* (Pictet, 1834)
SERICOSTOMATIDAE	NOTIDOBIA Stephens, 1829	* *ciliaris* (Linnaeus, 1761)
	SERICOSTOMA Latreille, 1825	*personatum* (Spence in Kirby & Spence, 1826)
ODONTOCERIDAE	ODONTOCERUM Leach, 1815	*albicorne* (Scopoli, 1763)
MOLANNIDAE	MOLANNA Curtis, 1834	*albicans* (Zetterstedt, 1840)
		(*M. palpata*)
		* *angustata* Curtis, 1834
LEPTOCERIDAE	ATHRIPSODES Billberg, 1820	*albifrons* (Linnaeus, 1758)
		aterrimus (Stephens, 1836)
		bilineatus (Linnaeus, 1758)
		cinereus (Curtis, 1834)
		commutatus (Rostock, 1874)
	CERACLEA Stephens, 1829 (ATHRIPSODES)	*albimacula* (Rambur, 1842)
		(*A. alboguttatus*)
		annulicornis (Stephens, 1836)
		dissimilis (Stephens, 1836)
		fulva (Rambur, 1842)
		nigronervosa (Retzius, 1783)
		senilis (Burmeister, 1839)
	LEPTOCERUS Leach, 1815	* *interruptus* (Fabricius, 1775)
		* *lusitanicus* (McLachlan, 1884)
		tineiformis Curtis, 1834
	MYSTACIDES Latreille, 1825	*azurea* (Linnaeus, 1761)
		longicornis (Linnaeus, 1758)
		* *nigra* (Linnaeus, 1758)
	ADICELLA McLachlan, 1877	* *filicornis* (Pictet, 1834)
		reducta (McLachlan, 1865)
	EROTESIS McLachlan, 1877	* *baltica* McLachlan, 1877
	TRIAENODES McLachlan, 1865	*bicolor* (Curtis, 1834)
	YLODES Milne, 1934 (TRIAENODES)	* *conspersus* (Rambur, 1842)
		reuteri (McLachlan, 1880)
		* *simulans* (Tjeder, 1929)
	OECETIS McLachlan, 1877	*furva* (Rambur, 1842)
		lacustris (Pictet, 1834)
		notata (Rambur, 1842)
		ochracea (Curtis, 1825)
		testacea (Curtis, 1834)
	SETODES Rambur, 1842	*argentipunctellus* McLachlan, 1877
		* *punctatus* (Fabricius, 1793)

COLLECTION, PRESERVATION AND EXAMINATION

Collection

Case-bearing caddis larvae live in all types of waterbody except the most temporary or polluted. Some species live in very small waterbodies such as inconspicuous trickles, shallow grassy marshes, ditches and pools that only hold water over winter, tiny pools between tussocks on bogs, sulphurous leaf-filled pools in woodland and even salt-marsh pools. One species, *Enoicyla pusilla*, is terrestrial.

Waterbodies can be worked with appropriately-sized nets but hand-searching, with the aid of a clear-bottomed viewing tube for deeper water, is usually the most productive. It is important to examine a wide range of habitats and include riffle, weedbeds, tree roots, submerged branches and logs, and on and under large stones. Hard objects lifted from the habitat for scrutiny can be particularly fruitful for attached larvae and pupae.

The larvae of almost all species are at an identifiable instar at some time between March and May and this is a good time for a faunal survey. Larvae can be transported alive in damp tissue paper or moss, or well-aerated water. They may leave their cases during this procedure; as the case is useful for identification it should not be discarded.

It is worth collecting pupal cases because, even if the pupa is immature or the adult has emerged, there is frequently enough of the larval exuviae (cast skin) to enable identification. Pupal cases are often attached to stones, logs or other objects and can be easier to find than larvae. Pupal cases from which the adult has emerged are best transported damp, as sclerites may be washed out in water.

Preparation of larvae for identification

Narcotisation. Living larvae can be identified, but killed and preserved larvae are much easier to deal with and all the keys in this book were prepared using preserved material. Making larvae insensible before placing them in preservative is more humane and also results in better specimens, as they are less contracted. A cheap and quick method is to place the caddis larvae directly into undiluted soda water.

Narcotisation is also useful to check that larvae are at a suitable instar for identification; if not, an attempt can be made to rear them.

Rearing. Almost all case-bearing caddis larvae are easy to rear. Unlike many caseless caddis, they do not require water circulation for feeding although aeration is desirable to prevent putrefaction of food. Shallow containers such as washing-up bowls are useful. Suitable foods include fallen leaves and dead grass for litter-feeding species, water starwort (*Callitriche*) or aquatic grasses for plant eaters, split wheat grains and slices of carrot. Although many species will eat meat only a few leptocerids are normally carnivorous and cannibalism, except of pupae, is rare. Species that graze organisms and fine detritus from surfaces are best fed by regularly supplying stones collected from their habitat. A range of materials for case-building should be provided.

Preservation. A 70 to 80% solution of industrial methylated spirits in water is good for killing and preserving caddis larvae. It is important to use a sufficient volume of the solution because the water present inside a larva or trapped within its case can cause serious dilution, resulting in dissolution of body contents and darkening of the sclerites in a year or so. Better fixatives exist, e.g. Kahle's and Pampel's fluids, but they are more toxic and unpleasant to use, and larvae stored in them long-term usually undergo serious colour changes. Preserved larvae should be stored in the dark to prevent bleaching.

When sending tubes of preserved larvae through the post it is essential to immobilise the contents with a paper tissue bung to prevent damage to the specimens or labels. Cotton wool should be avoided as larvae become entangled.

Examination of larvae. Larvae should be examined in fluid – tapwater for living larvae, and the same fluid in which they are stored for preserved larvae. Most characters can be seen without dismembering the larva if using a good-quality stereo microscope for magnifications up to x70; **good lighting is essential**. When higher magnifications are specified for a character, or for very small larvae, a slide mount can be prepared for use with a compound microscope. Alternatively the larva or detached part can be placed in a cell on a slide. A 50/50 mixture of glycerol and 70% industrial methylated spirits is a suitable temporary slide mountant for preserved larvae and their parts.

Removal of larvae from their cases. It is necessary to remove larvae from their cases for identification; most live larvae are reluctant to leave their cases and must first be narcotised or killed. Removal of a larva from its case must be done cautiously, even with dead larvae, as the anal proleg claws are often firmly hooked into the case and a sharp tug may tear the animal in two. Pushing the larva down the case before pulling will usually unhook the claws. Another method is to push the larva from the rear of the case with blunt forceps or a probe, though this may damage the end of the case.

If the larva is to be kept alive it must be replaced in its case after examination. This can only be achieved while it is still narcotised, as an active naked larva will resist being forced into a case and will rarely re-enter voluntarily.

When the keys seem to fail

The authors of these keys are always interested to see larvae that do not key out satisfactorily. Quite often, specimens that have been sent to us show that the problem lies not in the keys but is due to the poor state of the larvae. If the keys appear to have failed please check to see if your material falls into any of the following categories, where correct determination may be impossible.

Larvae preserved for long periods. It is best to identify larvae soon after collection. The rate of deterioration varies but all larvae that have been preserved for more than five years are likely to show some effects.

Where preservation conditions are ideal, deterioration may be restricted to subtle changes in patterning, such as darkening of sclerites and fading of pattern and spine colours. More serious darkening of sclerites can occur, particularly if initial alcohol concentrations were weak, or if the larva has been left to dry out and then re-wetted with preservative, or has been left too long in fixatives such as Kahle's fluid. Be especially cautious with larvae whose body contents have turned to 'mush'. Darkened specimens often lack the usual pale ring around the eye and are therefore easily recognisable.

Recently moulted larvae. After a moult, larvae take several hours to develop their characteristic patterning. Such larvae are pale in colour, and the application of light pressure with forceps to the head capsule or legs can easily deform them. They often distort during preservation and possess features such as curly setae, or patches of darkened cuticle around sites of injury. In a batch of larvae these specimens will clearly stand out as aberrant but single specimens can present serious problems to the inexperienced worker.

Asymmetrical larvae. Injury during life can result in left/right asymmetry of body parts. For gross abnormalities, e.g. stunted legs, it is easy to see which side should be ignored when taking the larva through the key, but be aware that more subtle distortions could be present.

Contracted specimens. During preservation, especially if narcotisation was not used and the larva is fully-fed, there can be serious contraction of the body so that features become hidden in inter-segmental folds. The labrum and especially the mandibles are problematical in contracted larvae as they will be retracted and need to be levered out into a normal position, possibly with the aid of a fine pin, before they can be examined.

'Dirty' larvae. Silt and iron oxide deposits may obscure important features and, if so, the deposits need to be carefully removed with a fine brush or forceps. Colonial protozoa and rotifers may infest larvae; as well as obscuring characteristic parts of the body they may resemble larval gill filaments and cause confusion.

GENERAL FEATURES OF CADDIS LARVAE

Body parts

Caddis larvae are distinguished from other insect larvae that have jointed thoracic legs by the presence of two *anal prolegs*, each bearing a single curved claw (see Fig. 4A). Parts of the body which are referred to in the keys are named in Figs 1–4; the nomenclature is basically that of Snodgrass (1935). A few points require explanation.

Most of the larval cuticle is thin chitin and is usually colourless, though it may have light reddish pigmentation in a few families. Thicker, sclerotized parts (*sclerites*) range from pale straw to dark brown. In all caddis larvae the prothoracic dorsum is covered by the heavily sclerotized *pronotum* (Fig. 1). The extent of sclerotization of the *mesodorsum* and *metadorsum* varies considerably from family to family; the sclerites are often paler than the pronotum. The sites of attachment of muscles to sclerites are sometimes marked by conspicuous spots of colour (*muscle attachment spots*) as, for example, in Figs 10A,C,D,F on page 33.

The cuticle bears two principal types of hair-like appendages. *Spines* arise as outgrowths of the cuticle and rarely become detached, though they may break.

Setae have a membranous articulating base surrounded by a sclerotized ring, the *alveolus*. They are comparatively easily detached and alveoli must be included in setal counts. *Pits* (seta-less sensory organs) superficially resemble alveoli. A small fixed number is present on each segment of all caddis larvae. Most are inconspicuous at normal magnification but attention is drawn to them where their inclusion in setal counts will affect the diagnosis.

Gills arise at specific positions on the abdominal segments (Fig. 4C) and their presence or absence at certain positions is often of taxonomic significance. In living larvae the *gill filaments* stand clear of the body surface and are further conspicuous by their silvery appearance due to air filling the tracheoles. However, in preserved larvae the tendency for shrinkage and loss of turgor by both body and gills, together with loss of air and collapse of the filaments against the body surface, call for special care when determining the number of filaments and their point of origin.

The number of occupied gill positions on the abdomen and the number of gill filaments present at each position can be significantly affected by the oxygen concentration of the larval environment. Wichard (1974) and Badcock *et al.* (1987) discuss this phenomenon in some detail. In the following keys, where a gill is stated as absent from the first or second abdominal segment, this is almost always constant for the species. However, on the posterior abdominal segments, gills may be completely absent or present at several positions, depending on the oxygen saturation levels normally prevalent in the particular waterbody. For example, expect to find a low number of gills in populations from a Scottish loch but expect the same species from a lake in south-east England to be well-endowed.

The *legs* consist of six elements (see Fig. 2); the *coxa* is proximal (nearest the body) and the *tarsal claw* is distal (furthest from the body). The *trochanter* and sometimes the *femur, tibia* and *tarsus* are subdivided, but they articulate as single elements.

Cases

The items that make up a caddis case are bound together by silk threads. In all families except Glossosomatidae there is an inner tube of silk to which the fragments are attached. This tube collapses if the fragments are removed. In a few caddis the case consists mainly or entirely of this secreted silken tube which in these particular species is strong and resilient. The form of the case is characteristic and, with experience, many caddis can be identified to species, genus or family using the case alone. However, *in extremis* all caddis can make a case from material they do not normally use and several caddis naturally produce a range of quite different cases depending on the materials that are available. The form of the case usually changes between early and late larval instars.

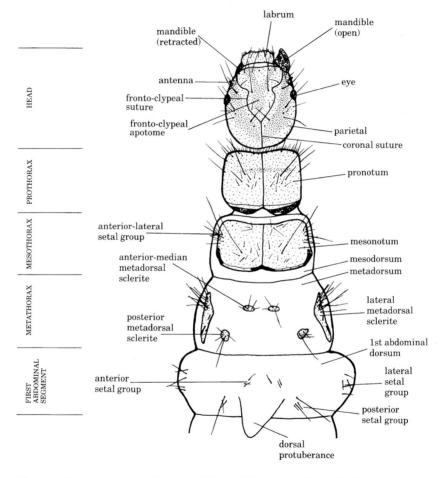

Fig. 1. Typical cased caddis larva (*Limnephilus lunatus*): head, thorax and 1st abdominal segment, dorsal view.

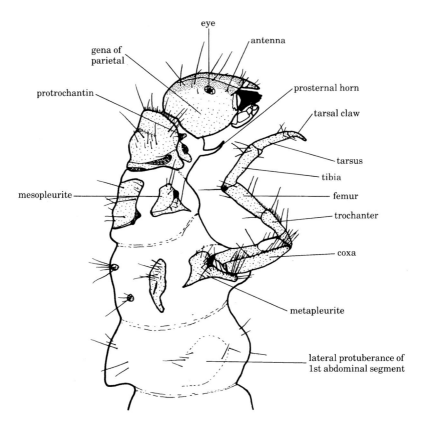

Fig. 2.   Typical cased caddis larva (*Limnephilus lunatus*): head, thorax and 1st abdominal segment, lateral view, (1st and 2nd legs omitted).

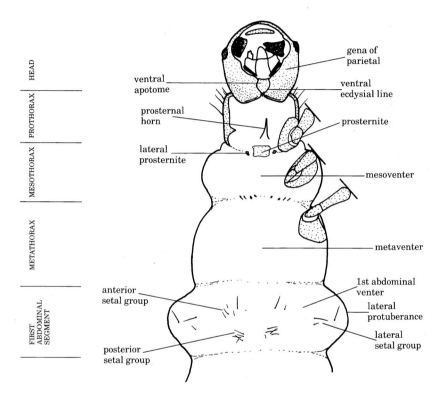

Fig. 3.   Typical cased caddis larva (*Limnephilus lunatus*): head, thorax and 1st abdominal segment, ventral view (legs omitted).

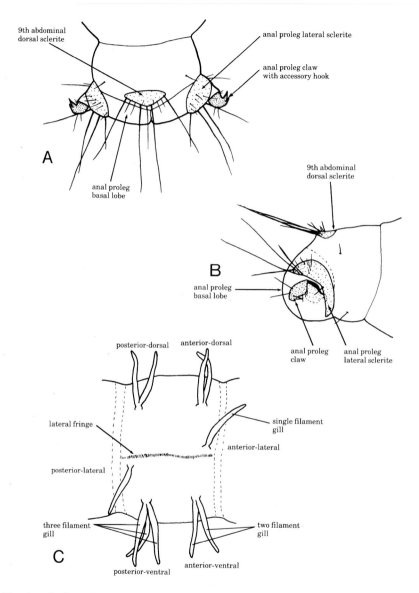

Fig. 4.   **A–C:** typical cased caddis larva (*Limnephilus lunatus*): A, 9th abdominal
          segment, dorsal view; B, 9th abdominal segment, lateral view; C, 4th
          abdominal segment, lateral view.

NOTES ON THE KEYS

General layout of the keys

Following an initial Key to Families, each family of case-bearing larvae is dealt with separately. Each Family Key is prefaced by a short introduction which users are urged to read carefully as it will enable them to check that they have arrived at the appropriate family. The introduction also gives general information on the biology of the family and draws attention to any features in the Family Key which may require particular care. After identification to species at appropriate couplets, brief notes are given in smaller type, describing additional features, such as head colour or the case, and giving information on habitat and distribution.

Larvae hold their heads and legs at various angles to the body but for the purposes of the keys the following conventions are adopted. The head is described as though it was extended with the mouth directed anteriorly (forwards) so that the surface that includes the fronto-clypeal apotome (Fig. 1) is dorsal. The legs are described as if extended at right-angles to the body with their broad faces directed anteriorly and posteriorly and with narrow dorsal and ventral edges. Text-figures are aligned with the anterior to the top of the page in dorsal and ventral views and to the right in lateral views. The distal end of leg elements lies to the right of the page. Mouthparts are normally omitted from drawings of the head. The text-figures show final-instar larvae unless otherwise stated.

Early instars and their identification

The great majority of caddis have five larval instars, each terminated by a moult. They are denoted instar I (first instar after hatching) to instar V (final larval instar before the moult to the pupa). Reported exceptions are *Sericostoma personatum* (at least six instars) and *Agapetus fuscipes* (seven instars). With successive moults there is a general tendency for colour and patterning of sclerites to become more distinct and for numbers of setae and gills to increase.

Most species can only be identified with confidence at later instars. There are examples where a species is characterised by possession of an attribute that is apparent in SOME specimens at an earlier instar than is recognised in the keys. Such well-developed specimens can be safely identified.

In each Family section, the range of headwidths (and number measured) is tabulated for different instars, based on British and Irish material. (Headwidth is the width of the head capsule at its widest point, excluding the eyes if they protrude beyond the outline of the head). Unless otherwise stated, all instars for which headwidth measurements are given can be identified to species, using the keys given in this publication.

At instar I, many of the family characteristics used in the keys are absent or poorly developed and these larvae are not considered here. Until recently the only general work on first-instar caddis larvae was Siltala (1907) but Hetrick *et al.* (1998) point the way towards further studies of these intriguing animals.

Biology

Descriptions of all British caddis were summarised by Wallace (1991), but information has been updated for this publication; records for Irish caddis come from J. P. O'Connor of the National Museum of Ireland, Dublin. When considering the habitat, it should be remembered that larvae may be carried by water movement into an atypical habitat and persist there for some time. A convention has been adopted for describing distribution: 'widespread' means that the species occurs throughout the British Isles, whilst 'throughout Britain' implies absence from Ireland.

Life cycles are outlined for each family to indicate when particular sizes of larvae are normally encountered. There is little published information on this (full life cycle data are available for only about 30 of the 152 species of case-bearing caddis) and we have relied heavily on our own observations. Life cycles may vary with location and the information given here should be taken only as a rough guide.

Sources of taxonomic information

Previously published keys form the basis of the present work. All have been revised to accommodate early instars, assist where difficulties are known to have existed in their use, and to achieve uniformity. A large number of specimens was examined during the course of the revision; most are now housed in Liverpool Museum.

Sources of information are given below.

General reference – Siltala (1907), Nielsen (1942), Hickin (1967), Lepneva (1971), Waringer & Graf (1997).

Key to Families – Wiggins (1977), with additional information from Edington & Hildrew (1995) (whose key separates groups of families of case-bearing caddis from caseless families and is satisfactory though difficult to use with some early-instar larvae and badly preserved material) and from Siltala (1907).

Beraeidae – Wiberg-Larsen (1979), with additional information from Morton (1890).

Brachycentridae – Only one species occurs in the British Isles.

Glossosomatidae – Mackereth (1956) and Pitsch (1993).

Goeridae – Hiley (1972), with additional information from Nielsen (1942).

Hydroptilidae – Marshall (1978), Nielsen (1948) and Wiggins (1977), with additional information from Barnard (1971), Giudicelli & Vaillant (1967) and Stroot (1989).

Lepidostomatidae – Hiley (1972).

Leptoceridae – Wallace (1981), with additional information from Wallace (1976).

Limnephilidae – Hiley (1976) and Wallace (1980), with additional information from Botosaneanu (1974) on *M. aspersus*, Garside (1979), Hiley (1973), Panzenbock & Waringer (1997), Wallace (1978), Wallace *et al*. (1985) and Wallace & Wallace (1985). G. B. Wiggins allowed us to use unpublished information about early-instar *Ironoquia* and N. Williams suggested the fronto-clypeal apotome character for *Halesus* species. L. Botosaneanu donated larvae of *M. aspersus* from the Canary Islands.

Molannidae – Leader (1968).

Odontoceridae – Only one species occurs in the British Isles.

Phryganeidae – Bray (1967), with additional information from Bray (1964), Gislason (1979) on *A. picta*, Solem (1971), Wallace & Wiggins (1978) and Wiggins (1998). G. Gislason donated larvae of *A. picta* from Iceland.

Sericostomatidae – Wallace (1977).

KEY TO FAMILIES

1   Pronotum with 5 setae on each side (include the alveoli of detached setae (see p. 14) but not the two pits, *p* in Fig. 5A, which are present at all instars); one of the five setae lies at the anterior-lateral corner and there are no other setae along the anterior edge (Figs 5A,B)—

INSTAR I
(first instar after hatching)

Hetrick *et al.* (1998) and Siltala (1907) will enable many first instars to be identified to Family level.

—   Pronotum with more than 5 setae on each side (some of which may be small and pale); more than 1 seta lies on the anterior edge (Figs 5C, 7E–H, 8F,G)—   **2**

2   Dorsum of each thoracic segment largely covered by sclerotized plates (Figs 5D, 6A–D)—   **3**

—   Metadorsum and sometimes mesodorsum entirely membranous or with widely spaced sclerites (e.g. Figs 7E–H, 8F,G)—   **5**

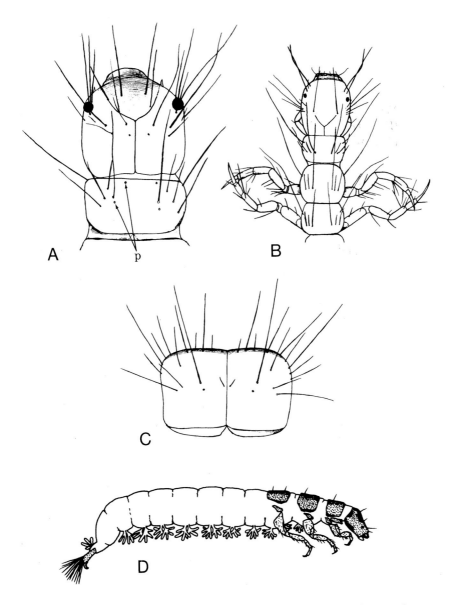

Fig. 5. **A:** head and pronotum, dorsal view, of *Nemotaulius punctatolineatus*, instar I. **B:** head and thorax, dorsal view, of *Plectrocnemia conspersa*, instar I. **C:** pronotum, dorsal view, of *N. punctatolineatus*, instar II. **D:** typical larva of the family Hydropsychidae, lateral view.

3   Ventro-lateral gills, branched at instars III–V, on abdominal segments
      (Fig. 5D). Anal proleg with a terminal brush of long setae at instars III–V
      (Fig. 5D)—   Caseless: Family HYDROPSYCHIDAE
                                                 (See Edington & Hildrew 1995)

—   No ventro-lateral gills on abdominal segments (Figs 6A,C). Anal proleg
      without a terminal brush of long setae (Figs 6A,C,D)—   **4**

4   9th abdominal dorsum with a sclerotized plate (arrow, Figs 6A,D,E)—
                                              Family HYDROPTILIDAE, p. 72
                                                            (Figs 6A,B,D)

      Seven types of larvae occur in the Hydroptilidae, all relatively small (maximum
      headwidth 0.4 mm and maximum case length 8 mm). Cases are distinctive in
      outline and most are laterally flattened (see text-figures on pp. 75, 77, 79, 81,
      83).

      Hydroptilidae instars II–IV are caseless, have prominent lateral setae, sclerites
      on the dorsa of abdominal segments 1–8, and slender anal proleg claws which
      are not sharply angled distally (see Fig. 6D).

—   9th abdominal dorsum without a sclerotized plate (Figs 6C,F)—
                                              Caseless: Family ECNOMIDAE
                                                 (See Edington & Hildrew 1995)

      Prominent lateral fringe of setae on abdominal segments 2–8 (Fig. 6C).

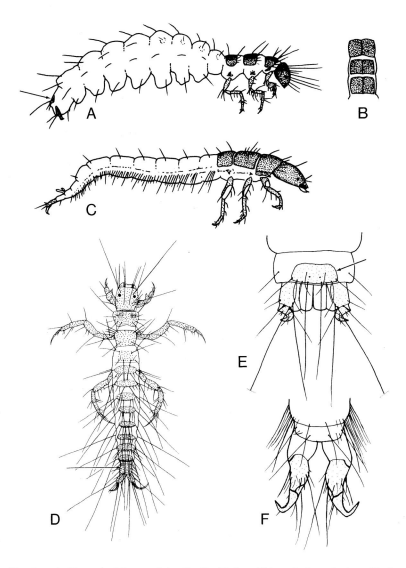

Fig. 6   **A, B:** typical larva of the family Hydroptilidae: A, lateral view; B, dorsal
sclerites of thorax. **C:** *Ecnomus tenellus* (Ecnomidae), lateral view of larva.
D, E: *Agraylea multipunctata* (Hydroptilidae): D, dorsal view of instar III; E,
9th abdominal segment, dorsal view, instar V. **F:** 9th abdominal segment,
dorsal view, of *Ecnomus tenellus* (Ecnomidae).

5(2) Larva can have ANY of the following features:

    (a) 1st abdominal segment with lateral and, usually, dorsal protuberances (*pr* in Figs 10H, 11A,C); lateral protuberance may bear a sclerite *s* (Fig. 10H).

    (b) Anal proleg short and squat, with a transversely aligned lateral sclerite *s* (Figs 7A–D).

    (c) Metadorsum with more than 2 anterior-lateral setae (arrow, Figs 7E–H)—   **8**

— Larva must have ALL of the following features:

    (a) 1st abdominal segment with neither lateral nor dorsal protuberances, nor a lateral sclerite (Figs 9A,B).

    (b) Anal proleg long and tapering, with a longitudinally aligned lateral sclerite *s* (Figs 8A–E).

    (c) Metadorsum with only 2 anterior-lateral setae (arrow, Figs 8F,G), one of which may be very small and pale—   **6**

Fig. 7. **A, B:** 9th abdominal segment of *Limnephilus lunatus* (Limnephilidae): A, dorsal view; B, lateral view. **C, D:** 9th abdominal segment of *Phryganea bipunctata* (Phryganeidae): C, dorsal view; D, lateral view. **E–H:** thoracic segments, dorsal view: E, *Potamophylax latipennis* (Limnephilidae); F, *Brachycentrus subnubilus* (Brachycentridae); G, *Beraea maurus* (Beraeidae); H, *Phryganea bipunctata* (Phryganeidae).

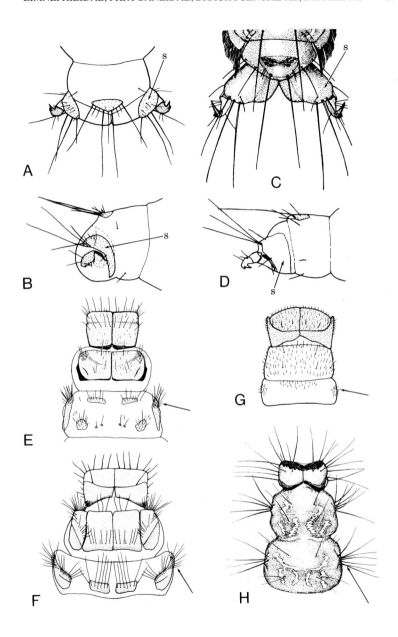

6   9th abdominal dorsum with sclerotized plate *n* (Figs 8B–D)—   **7**

—   9th abdominal dorsum without sclerotized plate (Figs 8A,E)—
                         Caseless: Families PHILOPOTAMIDAE,
                                             POLYCENTROPODIDAE,
                                                   PSYCHOMYIIDAE
                                    (See Edington & Hildrew 1995)

Fig. 8.   **A–E:**   9th   abdominal   segment: A,   *Plectrocnemia   conspersa*
          (Polycentropodidae), dorsal view; B, *Rhyacophila dorsalis* (Rhyacophilidae),
          dorsal view; C, *Agapetus fuscipes* (Glossosomatidae), dorsal view; D, *A.
          fuscipes*, lateral view; E, *Tinodes waeneri* (Psychomyiidae), lateral view. **F,
          G:** thoracic segments, dorsal view: F, *Plectrocnemia   conspersa*
          (Polycentropodidae); G, *Agapetus fuscipes* (Glossosomatidae).

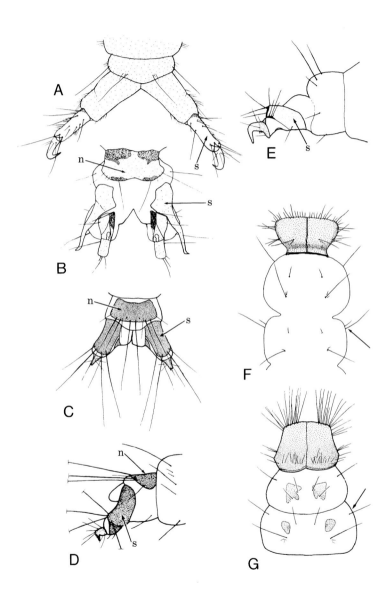

7   Branched gills present on abdominal segments (Fig. 9A). Prosternal
     plates absent—   Caseless: Family RHYACOPHILIDAE
                                              (See Edington & Hildrew 1995)

—   No gills present on abdominal segments (Fig. 9B). Prosternal plates
     prominent (arrows, Fig. 9C)—   Family GLOSSOSOMATIDAE, p. 54

Six species of Glossosomatidae occur in Britain, five in Ireland. Cases are
humped, with no difference between front and rear ends (see Figs 20C,D on p.
55). When collected, larvae frequently leave their cases when placed in
preservative or into still water in a sorting dish. The cases are quite fragile and
may be almost destroyed in certain sampling situations. On occasions, caseless
glossosomatids are also common components of the drifting fauna in streams.
Larvae are restricted to moderate and fast-flowing waters or, occasionally, stony
shores of lakes.

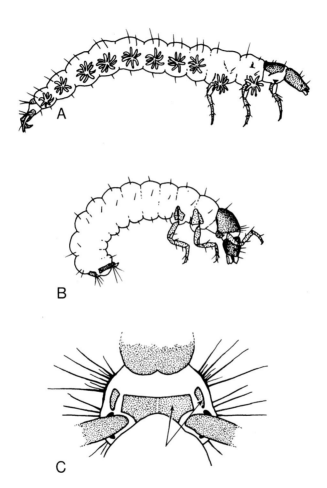

Fig. 9. **A:** typical larva of the family Rhyacophilidae, lateral view. **B:** typical larva of the family Glossosomatidae, lateral view. **C:** prothorax of *Agapetus fuscipes* (Glossosomatidae), ventral view.

8(5) *EITHER:* antenna slender* (arrow, Fig. 10A), at least six times longer
      than its width at widest part (excluding terminal seta, length *l* in Fig.
      10B), and always situated very close to anterior margin of head capsule;

      OR: mesonotum lightly pigmented except for a pair of dark, curved
      posterior-lateral projections (arrows, Fig. 10F; projections may be
      hidden in the intersegmental fold).

      (Some species have both characters.) —

                                              Family LEPTOCERIDAE, p. 88
                                                            (Figs 10G–I)
                              and *Beraeodes minutus* (Beraeidae), p. 44
      *NB: the antennae of ALL caddis larvae are small and relatively insignificant.

      Leptocerids are a diverse group of 31 species in Britain, 23 in Ireland. Larvae are
      quite small, with a maximum headwidth of 0.7 mm. Cases usually are up to 15
      mm long; if longer (to 30 mm), then no more than 2.5 mm wide. Legs, especially
      the 3rd legs, are long and held in front of the larva (Fig. 10H). In life, the small
      case with two slender legs protruding is characteristic (Fig. 10G).

—   Antenna not slender (arrow, Figs 10C–E), at most four times longer than
      its width at widest part (excluding terminal seta), sometimes situated
      some distance behind anterior margin of head capsule (arrow, Figs 10D,
      13A,C,D) AND mesonotum (if present) without curved posterior-lateral
      projections—   **9**

Fig. 10. **A, B:** *Athripsodes aterrimus* (Leptoceridae): A, head capsule; B, anterior-
       lateral region of head capsule. **C–E:** head capsule: C, *Molanna angustata*
       (Molannidae); D, *Goera pilosa* (Goeridae); E, *Beraea pullata* (Beraeidae). **F:**
       mesodorsum of *Ceraclea albimacula* (Leptoceridae). **G:** dorsal view of the
       anterior part of a leptocerid larva in its case, depicting the protruding tips of
       the long 3rd legs. **H, I:** typical larva of the family Leptoceridae; H, lateral
       view; I, dorsal sclerites of thorax.

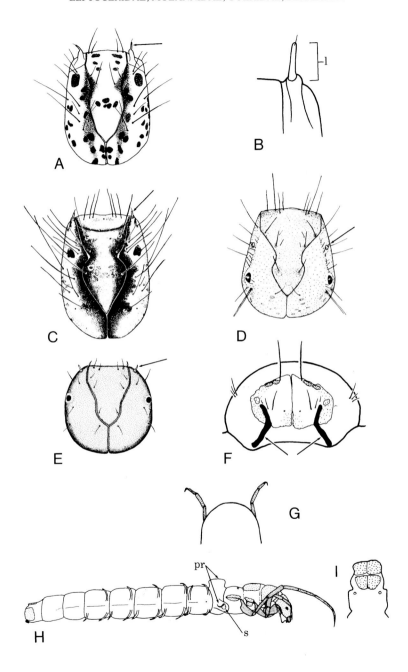

9   Mesodorsum and metadorsum largely unsclerotized (though they may be
     pigmented) and very similar to each other in both setal arrangement and
     colouration (Fig. 7H)—   Family PHRYGANEIDAE, p. 234
                                        (Figs 11A,B)

     Ten species of Phryganeidae occur in Britain, seven in Ireland. The most
     COMMONLY encountered larvae have a conspicuously banded head and
     pronotum, and inhabit a case made of cut fragments of vegetation arranged in a
     spiral; posterior ends of fragments may overhang and give the case a shaggy
     appearance (Figs 102A,B p. 237). Larvae are found only in still or slow-flowing
     water.

—   Mesodorsum largely covered by sclerotized plates (which may lack
     colour, particularly in small larvae) and different from the metadorsum
     in setal arrangement and often also in colour (Figs 7E–G)—   **10**

10   Mesopleurite with an anterior process *ap* which projects free from body
     wall (Figs 11C,D)—   Family GOERIDAE, p. 68

     Three species of Goeridae occur in Britain and Ireland. The anterior process on
     the mesopleurite makes the larvae unmistakable. The cases are strong and neatly
     constructed, with large ballast stones attached to the sides (Fig. 26A, p. 69).

—   Mesopleurite without an anterior process projecting free from body
     wall—   **11**

11   Tibia of *1st* leg with a ventral process (arrow, Fig. 11E) terminating in a
     strong seta. Tarsal claw of 3rd leg with several fine spines in addition to
     the basal seta *b* (Fig. 11G)—   Family MOLANNIDAE, p. 228
                                        (Figs 11H,I)

     Two species of Molannidae occur in Britain, one in Ireland. The winged cases
     are characteristic (Figs 99F–H, p. 229). However, the wings are fragile and may
     become broken during sampling. Larvae are restricted to still or very slow-
     flowing waters.

—   Tibia of *1st* leg without a ventral process (Fig. 11F). Tarsal claw of 3rd
     leg with only the basal seta *b* (as in Fig. 11F)—   **12**

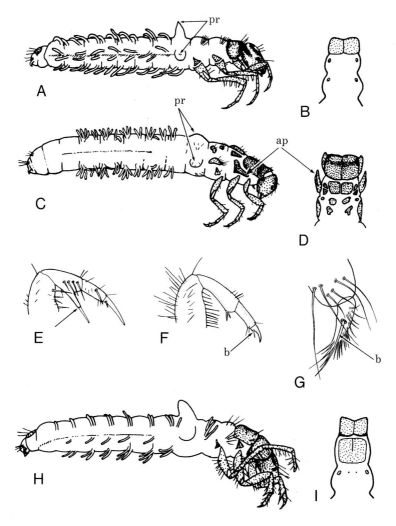

Fig. 11. **A, B:** typical larva of the family Phryganeidae: A, lateral view; B, dorsal sclerites of thorax. **C, D:** typical larva of the family Goeridae: C, lateral view; D, dorsal sclerites of thorax. **E, F:** tibia and tarsus of 1st leg, posterior view: E, *Molanna angustata* (Molannidae); F, *Odontocerum albicorne* (Odontoceridae). **G:** tarsal claw of 3rd leg, posterior view, of *M. angustata* (Molannidae). **H, I:** typical larva of the family Molannidae: H, lateral view; I, dorsal sclerites of thorax.

12   Tibiae of *2nd and 3rd* legs each with a ventral process (arrow, Figs
      12A,B) terminating in a strong seta. Metadorsum with sclerites and their
      associated setal groups arranged in a transverse curve (Figs 7F, 12C,E).
      1st abdominal segment with neither lateral nor dorsal protuberances—
                                    Family BRACHYCENTRIDAE, p. 50
                                                          (Figs 12D,E)

      One species occurs in Britain, none in Ireland. *Brachycentrus subnubilus* builds
      a straight smooth case (Figs 19A,B, p. 51) and lives in large streams and rivers.
      Only *Lepidostoma hirtum* (Lepidostomatidae) has a similar case and also lives
      in the same habitats.

—   Tibiae of *2nd and 3rd* legs and metadorsum not as above. 1st abdominal
      segment with lateral and (except in Lepidostomatidae) dorsal
      protuberances—   **13**

13   Anal proleg with a ventral brush of setae *b* just below the claw *c* (Fig.
      12H) and with a dorsal process (arrow, Fig. 12G) bearing setae, one of
      which is very much longer and stouter than the others. Pronotum with a
      flap-like anterior-lateral corner which (except in some larvae with a
      headwidth less than 0.3 mm) extends forwards as a lobe *l* and from
      which a sharp ridge runs obliquely backwards (Figs 12I,J)—
                                    Family BERAEIDAE, p. 44
                          except *Beraeodes minutus* (See couplet 8, above)

      Larvae keying out here are small, with plain orange or brick-coloured heads.
      Cases are curved, up to 10 mm long by 1.5 mm wide, and made from sand grains
      (Figs 18D,E, p. 49). Three species occur in Britain, two in Ireland.

—   Anal proleg with neither a brush of setae just below the claw *c*
      (Fig. 12F) nor a dorsal process. Pronotum with neither a flap-like
      anterior-lateral corner nor a sharp ridge, though the corner may be
      sharply angled or produced into a point—   **14**

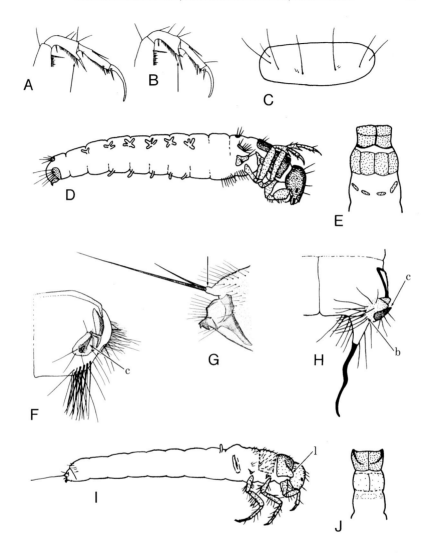

Fig. 12. **A–E:** *Brachycentrus subnubilus* (Brachycentridae): A, tibia and tarsus of 2nd leg; B, tibia and tarsus of 3rd leg; C, metadorsum, instar II; D, larva, lateral view; E, dorsal sclerites of thorax. **F–H:** 9th abdominal segment: F, *Sericostoma personatum* (Sericostomatidae), left side, ventral view; G, *Beraea maurus* (Beraeidae), lateral view; H, *Ernodes articularis* (Beraeidae), left side, ventral view. **I, J:** typical larva of the family Beraeidae: I, lateral view; J, dorsal sclerites of thorax.

14   Antenna* (arrow, Figs 13A,C,D) situated some distance behind anterior margin of head capsule. Prosternal horn present (arrow, Fig. 13F). Anterior-lateral corner of pronotum never sharply angled or produced to a point (Figs 13F,G)—   **15**

*NB. The antennae of ALL caddis larvae are relatively small and insignificant.

—   Antenna (arrow, Fig. 14I) situated very close to anterior margin of head capsule. Prosternal horn absent. Anterior-lateral corner of pronotum may be sharply angled or produced to a point (Figs 15A,D, p. 42)—   **16**

15   1st abdominal segment with a dorsal protuberance (arrow, Fig. 13G; this may have collapsed but will be visible as a wrinkle in dorsal view, arrow, Fig. 13H). Antenna (arrow, Fig. 13A) at least as close to anterior margin of head capsule as to eye (except in the terrestrial *Enoicyla pusilla*). Gena without a fold alongside the ventral apotome (Fig. 13B)—

Family LIMNEPHILIDAE, p. 131

(Figs 13G,H)

56 species of Limnephilidae occur in Britain, 40 in Ireland. A diverse group; many larvae grow to a large size, with headwidths over 1 mm and cases approaching 3 cm x 1 cm.

—   1st abdominal segment without a dorsal protuberance (Figs 13I,J). Antenna (arrow, Figs 13C,D) situated very close to anterior margin of the eye. Gena with a fold *f* (Fig. 13E) alongside the ventral apotome (this fold is not always obvious in pale larvae)—

Family LEPIDOSTOMATIDAE, p. 84

(Figs 13I,J)

Three species of Lepidostomatidae occur in Britain and Ireland. The two commonest species make straight cases that are partly or entirely square in cross-section, a feature shared only with Brachycentridae.

Fig. 13. **A, B:** head capsule of *Limnephilus auricula* (Limnephilidae): A, dorsal view; B, ventral view. **C–E:** *Lepidostoma hirtum* (Lepidostomatidae): C, left eye and antenna; D, head capsule; E, ventral apotome and adjoining areas of genae. **F–H:** typical larva of the family Limnephilidae: F, head and thorax, lateral view, 1st leg omitted to show prosternal horn; G, larva, lateral view; H, dorsal sclerites of thorax and protuberances of 1st abdominal segment. **I, J:** typical larva of the family Lepidostomatidae: I, lateral view; J, dorsal sclerites of thorax and protuberances of 1st abdominal segment.

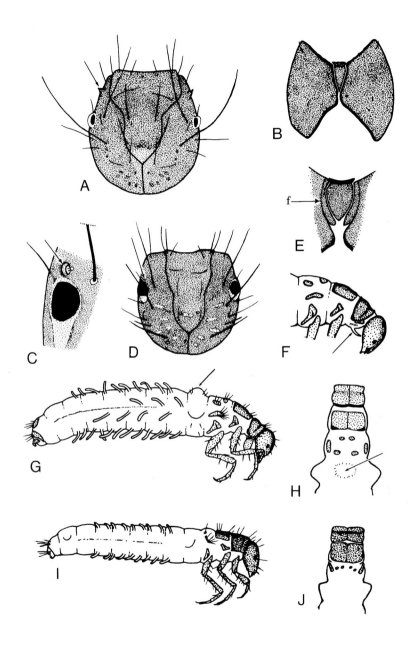

NOTE: Larvae in both of the following families have curved cases built with grains of sand (Fig. 101C–E on p. 233 and Figs 107A,B on p. 249).

16(14) Anal proleg claw with accessory hooks and a sharply angled crook (Figs 14A–D). Anal proleg with more than 5 setae *ds* on the dorsum (Figs 14A,B) except when headwidth is less than 0.25 mm. Protrochantin *pt* large with an upturned tip (Figs 15A–C). (Fronto-clypeal apotome dark brown except in some larvae with headwidth less than 0.5 mm, never with an anchor-shaped mark)—

Family SERICOSTOMATIDAE, p. 247
(Figs 15G,H)

Two species of Sericostomatidae occur in Britain, one in Ireland. Larvae occur in both still and flowing waters.

—   Anal proleg claw without accessory hooks and with a gently curved crook (Figs 14E–H). Anal proleg never with more than 5 setae *ds* on the dorsum (Figs 14E,F). Protrochantin *pt* small, without an upturned tip (Figs 15D–F). (Fronto-clypeal apotome pale with a distinct anchor-shaped mark, Fig. 14I, except in larvae with headwidth less than 0.9 mm.)—

Family ODONTOCERIDAE, p. 232
(Figs 15I,J)

One species of Odontoceridae occurs in Britain and Ireland: *Odontocerum albicorne*. Larvae are found only in stony streams and rivers.

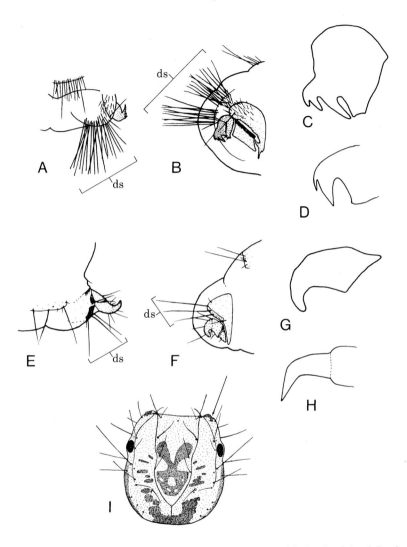

Fig. 14. **A–D:** *Sericostoma personatum* (Sericostomatidae): A, 9th abdominal segment, right side, dorsal view; B, 9th abdominal segment, lateral view; C, anal proleg claw; D, anal proleg claw, instar ?II. **E–I:** *Odontocerum albicorne* (Odontoceridae): E, 9th abdominal segment, right side, dorsal view; F, 9th abdominal segment, lateral view; G, anal proleg claw; H, anal proleg claw, instar II; I, head capsule.

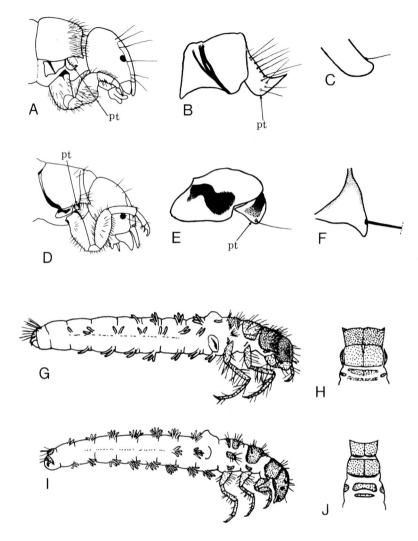

Fig. 15. **A–C:** *Sericostoma personatum* (Sericostomatidae): A, head and prothorax, lateral view; B, propleurites; C, protrochantin, instar ?II. **D–F:** *Odontocerum albicorne* (Odontoceridae): D, head and prothorax, lateral view; E, propleurites; F, protrochantin, instar II. **G, H:** typical larva of the family Sericostomatidae: G, lateral view; H, dorsal sclerites of thorax. **I, J:** *Odontocerum albicorne* (Odontoceridae): I, larva, lateral view; J, dorsal sclerites of thorax.

KEYS TO SPECIES

Key to 3 genera and 4 species of Beraeidae: page 44.

Key to 1 genus and 1 species of Brachycentridae: page 50.

Key to 2 genera and 6 species of Glossosomatidae: page 54.

Key to 2 genera and 3 species of Goeridae: page 68.

Key to 7 genera and 4 of 31 species of Hydroptilidae: page 72.

Key to 3 genera and 3 species of Lepidostomatidae: page 84.

Key to 10 genera and 31 species of Leptoceridae: page 88.

Key to 21 genera and 58 species of Limephilidae: page 131.

Key to 1 genus and 2 species of Molannidae: page 228.

Key to 1 genus and 1 species of Odontoceridae: page 232.

Key to 6 genera and 10 species of Phryganeidae: page 234.

Key to 2 genera and 2 species of Sericostomatidae: page 247.

KEY TO FAMILY BERAEIDAE
(THREE GENERA AND FOUR SPECIES)

Four species occur in the family Beraeidae (Table 1, p. 46). The larvae are found among moss and dead leaves in springs, and amidst dense vegetation and roots in flowing marshes and at the edges of streams and rivers. Larvae of *Beraeodes minutus* are also found among the roots of emergent vegetation in ponds and lakes. They are small, with curved tapering cases, up to 1 cm long, which are made of sand-grains (Figs 16C, 18D,E).

Two of the three genera, *Beraea* and *Ernodes,* have striking orange or brick-coloured heads and share several distinctive characters. The pronotum has a sharp ridge marking off the flap-like anterior-lateral corner which (except in instar II *Beraea)* extends forwards as a lobe (Figs 16E,F). The anal proleg has a posteriorly-directed dorsal process bearing setae, one of which is much longer and stouter than the others (Figs 17D–F). In ventral view the anal proleg claw has a brush of dark setae arising from a membranous area at its base (*b*, Fig. 17B). Other cased caddis larvae have only five setae around the claw and another three pale setae below the point (as in Fig. 12F). Very young sericostomatids have pale brown heads and superficially resemble *Beraea* and *Ernodes,* but the anal proleg lacks all three features described above. *Sericostoma personatum* is occasionally found with *Beraea.* (Certain microscopical characters of the larvae suggest an affinity between Beraeidae and Sericostomatidae, most notably the peculiar form of the lateral line which is illustrated by Denis (1984).

The third genus, *Beraeodes,* lacks many of the features which characterise other beraeids; it resembles leptocerids in its slender appearance, long antennae and third pair of legs (Figs 16A,C). The mosaic pattern on the pronotum, at least at the final instar (Fig. 16B), and the numerous setae on the fronto-clypeal apotome (Fig. 35G, p. 93), readily distinguish this larva from the leptocerids. The flight period of beraeids is quite short, from early to mid summer, but final-instar larvae of *Beraea* and *Ernodes* can be found during most of the year. It seems likely that some species require more than one year for the life cycle; half-grown larvae of *E. articularis* have been found during the adult flight period. Wiggins (1977) reported a similar observation for the North American *Beraea fontana* Wiggins.

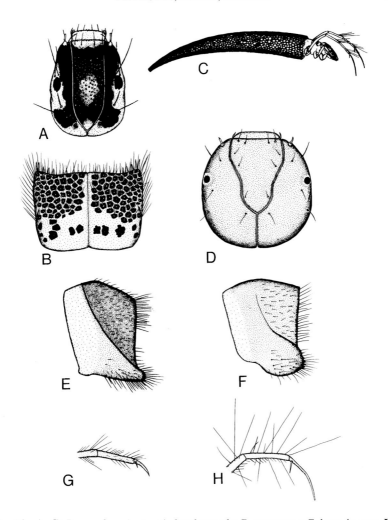

Fig. 16. **A–C:** *Beraeodes minutus*: A, head capsule; B, pronotum; C, larva in case. **D:** head capsule of *Beraea pullata*. **E, F:** pronotum, lateral view: E, *Ernodes articularis*; F, *Beraea pullata*. **G, H:** tarsus and claw of 3rd leg, posterior view: G, *Ernodes articularis*; H, *B. pullata*.

Table 1. Headwidths of Beraeidae: ranges (mm) (and *n*) for instars II to V.

Species	Instar II	Instar III	Instar IV	Instar V
Beraea maurus	—	0.34–0.43 (4)	0.52–0.55 (3)	0.59–0.74 (16)
Beraea pullata	0.18–0.27 (7)	0.43 (1)	—	0.83–0.90 (6)
Beraeodes minutus	—	—	0.32–0.42 (3)	0.51–0.59 (18)
Ernodes articularis	0.24 (1)	0.31–0.41 (7)	0.56 (1)	0.72–0.79 (5)

KEY TO LARVAE

1   Head with extensive black areas (Fig. 16A). Pronotum with a dark
     mosaic pattern (Fig. 16B), (less conspicuous at early instars than at instar
     V). Anal proleg with neither a ventral brush of dark setae below the claw
     (Fig. 17A) nor any dorsal seta which is very much longer and stouter
     than the others (Fig. 17C)—   **Beraeodes minutus** (L.)

     Associated with submerged roots of emergent vegetation, e.g. tree roots, in
     shallow water at the edges of rivers, streams, lakes and large ponds. Widespread.

—   Head without extensive black areas, uniformly straw to red-brown in
     colour (Fig. 16D). Pronotum without a black mosaic pattern, similar in
     colour to the head (Figs 16E,F). Anal proleg with a ventral brush of dark
     setae *b* below the claw *c* (Fig. 17B) and one dorsal seta which is very
     much longer and stouter than the others (Figs 17D–F)—   **2**

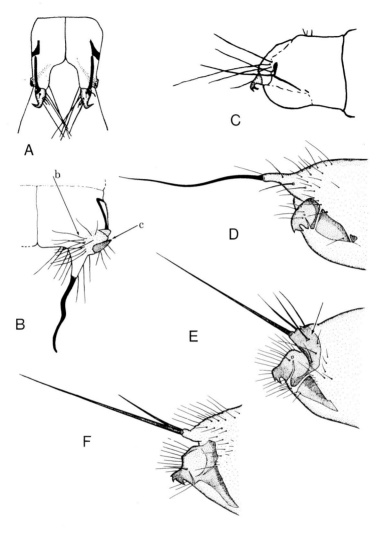

Fig. 17. **A, B:** 9th abdominal segment, ventral view: A, *Beraeodes minutus*; B, *Ernodes articularis*. **C–F:** 9th abdominal segment, lateral view: C, *B. minutus*; D, *E. articularis*; E, *Beraea pullata*; F, *Beraea maurus*.

2   Posterior end of case with a hemispherical prominence on which the
       opening is situated ventrally (Figs 18D,F). Pronotum with a bluntly
       pointed anterior-lateral corner (which extends forwards as a lobe at
       instars II–V, Fig. 16E). Anal proleg claw with 1 erect accessory hook
       (arrow, Fig. 18A)—   **Ernodes articularis** (Pictet)

       Head reddish-brown at instars IV and V, straw-coloured at instars II and III. 3rd
       leg with tarsus longer than claw at instars IV and V (Fig. 16G), similar in length
       at instars II and III. Longest seta of anal proleg dorsal process is black and
       sinuous (Figs 17B, D).

       Occurs among moss and fallen leaves in small springs and trickles of hard water,
       especially where travertine is depositing. Rare; scattered sites in Wales, southern
       England and Cheshire. *Beraea maurus* is often found with *Ernodes articularis*.

—   Posterior end of case without a hemispherical prominence (Figs 18E,G).
       Pronotum with a broadly rounded anterior-lateral corner (which extends
       forwards as a lobe at instars III–V, Fig. 16F; headwidth more than 0.3
       mm). Anal proleg claw with *EITHER* 2 erect accessory hooks *OR* 1
       decumbent accessory hook (arrows, Figs 18B,C)—   **3**

       Head orange or reddish-orange at instars IV and V, straw-coloured at instars II
       and III. 3rd leg with tarsus about as long as claw at instar V (Fig. 16H), shorter
       than claw at instars II–IV. Longest seta of anal proleg dorsal process is orange to
       dark brown and straight (Figs 17E,F); (the seta may be distorted in preserved
       material, particularly in prepupae and recently moulted specimens).

3   Anal proleg claw with one decumbent accessory hook (arrow, Fig. 18B).
       Anal proleg dorsal process with 3 setae which are about one-third as
       long as the largest seta (Fig. 17E); (there are also some very small dorsal
       setae which are never numerous)—   **Beraea pullata** (Curtis)

       Anal proleg dorsal process with a brownish sclerite at instars IV and V
       (arrow, Fig. 17E).

       Occurs among dense vegetation in flowing marshes, springs and at the edges of
       streams. Widespread and common.

—   Anal proleg claw with two erect accessory hooks (arrows, Fig. 18C).
       Anal proleg dorsal process with one seta which is about half as long as
       the largest seta (Fig. 17F); (there are also some very small setae which
       are numerous at instar V)—   **Beraea maurus** (Curtis)

       Anal proleg dorsal process without an obvious sclerite at any instar (Fig. 17F).
       Occurs among moss and fallen leaves in small springs and trickles, often with
       Crunoecia irrorata. Widespread and common.

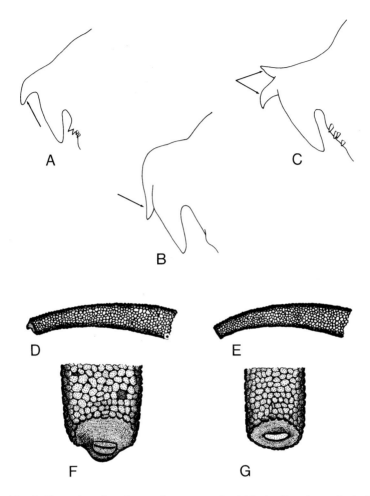

Fig. 18. **A–C:** anal proleg claw and accessory hook(s): A, *Ernodes articularis*; B, *Beraea pullata*; C, *B. maurus*. **D, E:** case, lateral view: D, *E. articularis*; E, *B. pullata*. **F, G:** posterior end of case, ventral view: F, *E. articularis*; G, *B. pullata*.

KEY TO FAMILY BRACHYCENTRIDAE
(ONE GENUS AND SPECIES)

The only British representative of this family is **Brachycentrus subnubilus** Curtis (Table 2, p. 52). It is widely distributed in rivers and large streams, where it is often present in considerable numbers. The species has not been recorded from Ireland.

The case of the full-grown larva is tubular and composed almost entirely of secretion, though this has an uneven texture and appearance due particularly to the presence of small pieces of plant material embedded within it (Fig. 19A). At early instars the case is rectangular in section and constructed of transversely arranged plant material held together by secretion (Fig. 19B); it is rather like the case of final-instar *Lepidostoma hirtum* (Fig. 33E, p. 87).

Brachycentrus subnubilus can be recognised by the presence, on the tibiae of the *second* and *third* legs, of a distal-ventral process terminating in a strong seta (Figs 12A,B, p. 37). The pronotum has a curved transverse ridge which is visible from instar II as a thin line on the dorsum (Fig. 12E). At instars IV and V the mesonotum is clearly divided into four sclerites and the metadorsum has four sclerites arranged in a transverse curve (Fig. 12E); at earlier instars the sclerites are pale and difficult to see but the position of those on the metadorsum is indicated by their associated setae (Fig. 12C). Anterior metadorsal sclerites and setae are absent at all instars. The first abdominal segment differs from that of most other cased caddis larvae in lacking dorsal and lateral protuberances. At later instars, the head has a distinctive pattern (Fig. 19C).

The larvae of *B. subnubilus* have a method of feeding which is unlike that used by any other British caddis. The case is attached to a substratum, such as a weed stem or a tree root, in flowing water with its anterior end facing into the current (Fig. 19D). The long second and third legs are extended outwards (as in Figs 19E,F) and, by virtue of the fine spines on their femora, form a filter mechanism which captures particles from the water stream. Murphy (1919), working with the North American species *B. nigrisoma* Banks which is morphologically similar to *B. subnubilus,* has described in detail how material so caught is removed and transferred to the mouth by the first legs, which are also provided with fine spines. Larger particles and organisms, including copepods, cladocerans and hydracarines, are seized between the second and third legs, assisted by their long claws and tibial spines, and then devoured. The long setae of the thorax and first abdominal segment probably prevent the case from becoming clogged by water-borne debris.

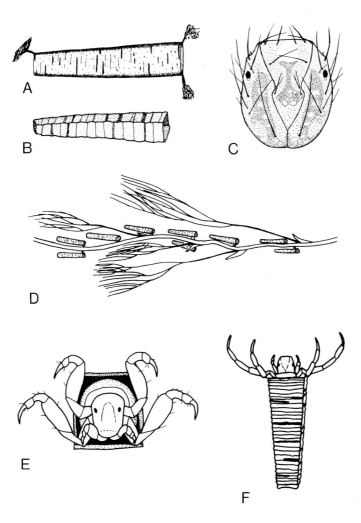

Fig. 19. **A, B:** case of *Brachycentrus subnubilus*: A, instar V; B, instar III. **C:** head of *B. subnubilus*. **D:** several cases of *B. subnubilus* attached to *Ranunculus* weed. **E, F:** feeding attitude of *B. nigrisoma:* E, anterior view; F, dorsal view.

If abundant debris has collected, the larva of *B. nigrisoma* will partially withdraw from its case and clean off material adhering to the anterior segments. Casual observations by one of us (IDW) indicate similar behaviour by *B. subnubilis*. The larvae can also detach their cases and move to a new site when there is an adverse change in current.

The adult flight period is in spring. Larvae appear soon afterwards and some reach the final instar by late autumn. Growth seems to continue during the winter.

Table 2. Headwidths of Brachycentridae: ranges (mm) (and *n*) for instars II to V of *Brachycentrus subnubilus*.

* Larvae with headwidths in this range could not be reliably separated into instars.

Instar II	Instar III	* Instars IV and V
0.25–0.31 (5)	0.36–0.47 (4)	0.67–1.19 (86)

A key to the Family Glossosomatidae begins on page 54.

KEY TO FAMILY GLOSSOSOMATIDAE
(TWO GENERA AND SIX SPECIES)

The family Glossosomatidae is closely related to families that have caseless larvae. This relationship is reflected in features such as the elongate form of the anal proleg lateral sclerite (*s* in Fig. 20G) and absence of protuberances on the first abdominal segment. The mandibles lack large teeth (Figs 20A,B) and the larvae feed on organisms and fine detritus scraped from surfaces.

The characteristic cases (Figs 20C,D) are abundant and conspicuous on stones in streams and rivers. Both openings of the case are alike and the larva regularly reverses its position. The spaces between sand grains are not completely filled by silk, as in other cased caddis, which enables oxygenated water to flow easily through the case. If placed in still water the larvae usually will leave their cases.

Agapetus cases differ from those of *Glossosoma* in having a loose collar of sand grains at each opening (Figs 20E,F) which collapses when the larva retreats, closing the entrance. Glossosomatid cases are not continuously enlarged as in other case-bearing families; each instar builds a larger case, attached to one end of the existing case, then bites off the old one (Anderson & Bourne 1974). For pupation the larva cuts away the underside of the case and fixes the rim of the upper dome to a stone. A brown cocoon is constructed inside this shelter. *Glossosoma* pupal shelters are 9 to 12 mm long while those of *Agapetus* range from 5 to 7 mm (exceptionally 3.5 to 9 mm in *A. fuscipes*).

Glossosoma boltoni, *G. conformis* and the three *Agapetus* species are widespread. In some stony rivers it is possible to find all five in the same sample. Adults have been collected from spring to autumn, but large larvae are most numerous in spring. There may be more than one generation a year. The rare *G. intermedium* has a short spring flight period and overwinters as a full-grown larva in a pupal cocoon. (*G. boltoni* and *A. fuscipes* can also be found in this state during winter, so the habit is by no means diagnostic).

Nielsen (1942) recorded seven larval instars in Danish *A. fuscipes* but Anderson & Bourne (1974) found only five headwidth groups in the North American *A. bifidus* Denning. It is not known how many instars are undergone by *Agapetus* species in the British Isles; hence the instars are denoted as final, final −1 and final −2 in Table 3 (p. 57). *Glossosoma* appears to have the usual five larval instars; the authors have found five distinct headwidth groups, including instar I.

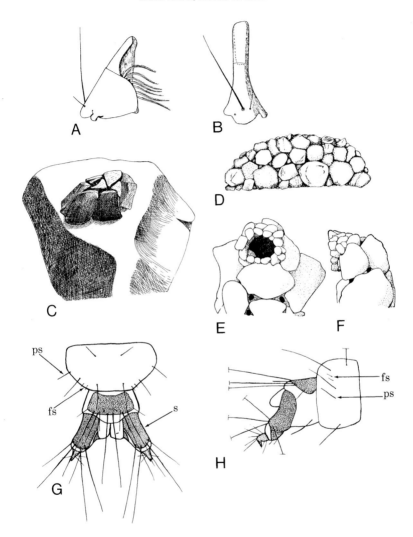

Fig. 20. **A, B:** right mandible of *Agapetus fuscipes*: A, ventral view; B, lateral view. **C:** pupal case of *Glossosoma intermedium* attached to a stone. **D–F:** larval case of *A. fuscipes:* D, lateral view; E, ventral view of opening; F, lateral view of opening. **G, H:** 8th and 9th abdominal segments of *A. fuscipes*: G, dorsal view; H, lateral view.

Separation of genera and species

Separation of the two genera is straightforward. Separation of the species is more difficult and the following points should be read before tackling the key.

Pronotal characters. The pronotum has a small area of thickening where it abuts the coxa and this is associated with a very darkly pigmented mark *(m*, Fig. 23F, p. 63 and Fig. 25A, p. 67). The extent of the mark (which is larger than the thickened area) is useful in identifying all six species. It is important not to confuse the mark *m* with the darkly coloured pleurite *pe* or proximal tip of the coxa *c* which in some poses lie just under the edge of the pronotum and are visible through it (Figs 23F, 25A). In *Agapetus* the pronotum in the vicinity of the mark may be deeper brown than most of the rest of the sclerite but only the region which is as dark as the band associated with the posterior pronotal groove (*b*; Figs 25A–C) is regarded as constituting the mark. In *Glossosoma* neither the mark nor the characters concerning the posterior pronotal band can be used with recently moulted specimens, as typical colouration takes some time to develop. Such specimens may be recognised by the presence of a very small lateral mark which does not incorporate the outer seta *os* (see Figs 23F–H for position of the outer seta).

Eighth abdominal segment. The posterior-lateral seta *ps* of the eighth abdominal segment is inconspicuous in some species and relatively prominent in others. The setae on the segment are best viewed from behind (Figs 24A–C, p. 65). Seta *ps* is easily detached by rough treatment, for example during collection by kick sampling, and may be missing, especially if any of the six large dorsal setae show evidence of damage.

Third abdominal segment. A prominent lateral seta on the third abdominal segment distinguishes *Agapetus fuscipes* larvae from those of the other two species (Fig. 24G, p. 65). In other species it is present only on the first and second segments (Fig. 24H). Like the characteristic setae described for the eighth abdominal segment, these may be absent from larvae that have been handled roughly during sampling and preservation.

Tarsal claw. The form of the basal seta of the tarsal claw is useful in separating the *Agapetus* species. Just after a moult, all three species have setae with tapering flexuous tips. *Agapetus fuscipes* usually retains this form (Fig. 24D) whilst in *A. ochripes* the flexuous tip wears away quickly, though the residual part of the seta may be curved (Fig. 24F). (Wear in *A. delicatulus* is very variable). All *Agapetus* species may be found with severely worn setae and claws (as in Fig. 24E) and the character should not be used in such larvae.

Table 3. Headwidths of Glossosomatidae: ranges (mm) (and *n*) for various instars. (Explanation for *Agapetus* instars is given on p. 54).

*Not keyed to species at this instar.

†*Agapetus fuscipes* is very variable in size. Some final-instar larvae (from very small mountain streams) had the same headwidths as penultimate-instar larvae from lowland sites and are not included in the table.

Species	Final instar −2	Final instar −1	Final instar
Agapetus delicatulus	*0.23–0.25 (10)	0.32–0.40 (30)	0.46–0.52 (40)
Agapetus fuscipes	*0.27–0.30 (25)	0.32–0.43 (50)	†0.47–0.54 (50)
Agapetus ochripes	*0.19–0.20 (3)	*0.25–0.28 (15)	0.36–0.45 (50)

Species	Instar II	Instar III	Instar IV	Instar V
Glossosoma boltoni	*0.19–0.22 (3)	*0.29–0.31 (5)	0.42–0.52 (25)	0.61–0.72 (25)
Glossosoma conformis	*0.20–0.22 (4)	*0.31–0.34 (6)	0.50–0.53 (10)	0.66–0.77 (15)
Glossosoma intermedium	—	*0.34 (1)	0.50–0.53 (6)	0.63–0.72 (12)

KEY TO LARVAE

1   Each side of pronotum with up to 7 setae along anterior margin (Fig.
     21A). Mesodorsum and metadorsum without median sclerites. Basal seta
     of tarsal claw arises from a prominence (arrow, Figs 21D,E). Gena with
     a line (arrow, Fig. 21G) alongside median ventral ecdysial line —
                                                Genus GLOSSOSOMA, 2

     Glossosoma species are not separable at instars II and III: headwidth less than 0.4
     mm.

—   Each side of pronotum with more than 7 setae along anterior margin (Fig.
     21B), (except in some larvae of headwidth less than 0.15 mm).
     Mesodorsum and metadorsum with median sclerites (arrows, Fig. 21C);
     (sclerites may not be apparent in larvae of headwidth less than 0.25 mm).
     Basal seta of tarsal claw does not arise from a prominence (Figs 21F,
     24D-F, p. 65). Gena without a line alongside median ventral ecdysial line
     (Fig. 21H)—   Genus AGAPETUS, 4

     Agapetus species are not separable when headwidth is less than 0.3 mm.

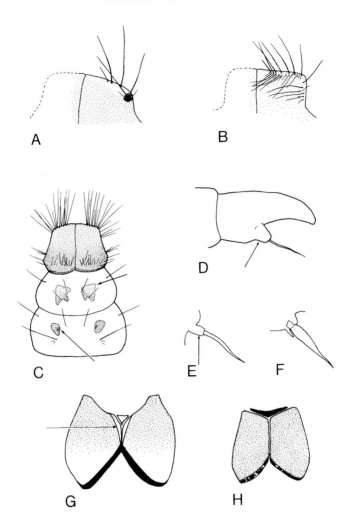

Fig. 21. **A, B:** pronotum, anterior part of right half: A, *Glossosoma boltoni*; B, *Agapetus fuscipes*. **C:** thorax of *A. fuscipes*, dorsal view. **D:** tarsal claw of *G. conformis*. **E, F:** basal seta of tarsal claw: E, *G. conformis*, instar II; F, *A. delicatulus*. **G, H:** head capsule, ventral view: G, *G. boltoni*; H, *A. delicatulus*.

2   9th abdominal dorsal sclerite with outermost setae (arrows, Fig. 22A)
     much shorter and thinner than the six large intermediate setae —
                                Glossosoma intermedium (Klapálek)
                                                    Instars IV and V

Fronto-clypeal apotome with lateral bulge (arrow, Fig. 22C). Dark lateral mark
of pronotum narrow, extending inwards about half way between outer seta *os* and
inner seta *is* (Fig. 23G). On the pronotum, the black band *b* associated with the
posterior groove fades completely or narrows considerably towards the median
suture; the area posterior to the band in region *R* is usually darker than the
opposing area anterior to the band (Fig. 23C). 8th abdominal segment with
posterior-lateral seta *ps* pale, not normally visible, smaller than the small fine
dorsal setae *fs* (as in Fig. 22E).

Rare; the only recent records are from two small streams in the English Lake
District, Cumbria.

—   9th abdominal dorsal sclerite with outermost setae (arrows, Fig. 22B)
     similar in length and thickness to the six large, intermediate setae —   **3**

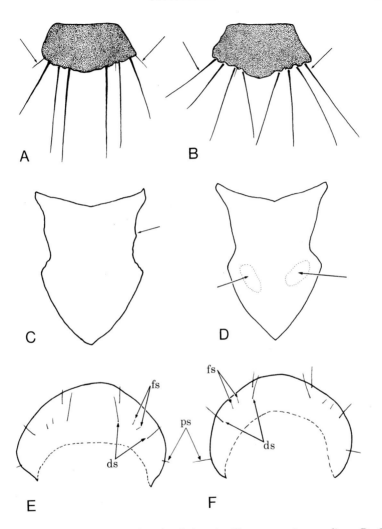

Fig. 22. **A, B:** 9th abdominal dorsal sclerite: A, *Glossosoma intermedium*; B, *G. boltoni*. **C, D:** fronto-clypeal apotome: C, *G. intermedium*; D, *G. boltoni*. **E, F:** 8th abdominal segment, posterior-dorsal view: E, *G. conformis*; F, *G. boltoni*.

3   8th abdominal segment with posterior-lateral seta *ps* inconspicuous, paler than the large dorsal setae *ds* and rarely longer than the small, fine dorsal setae *fs* (Fig. 22E). Region *R* of posterior margin of pronotum either entirely black (Fig. 23A) or with any brown pigment posterior to the dark band *b*, associated with the posterior groove, darker than pigment of opposing area anterior to the band (Fig. 23B); the band usually extends to the median suture (Figs 23A,B) —

Glossosoma conformis Neboiss
Instars IV and V

Dark lateral mark of pronotum frequently extends further inwards than inner seta *is* and usually shades into the general colour of the sclerite (Fig. 23H). Posterior part of fronto-clypeal apotome without pale areas.

Stony substratum in streams and rivers. Widespread and common in northern and western Britain, rare elsewhere.

—   8th abdominal segment with posterior-lateral seta *ps* as dark as the large dorsal setae *ds* and usually longer than the small, fine dorsal setae *fs* (Fig. 22F). Region *R* of posterior margin of pronotum never entirely black and with any brown pigment posterior to the dark band *b*, associated with the posterior groove, similar in shade to pigment of opposing area anterior to the band (Figs 23D,E); the band usually fades completely or narrows considerably towards the median suture (Figs 23D,E) —

Glossosoma boltoni Curtis
Instars IV and V

Dark lateral mark of pronotum rarely extends further inwards than inner seta *is* and usually has a distinct edge, not shading into the general colour of the sclerite (Fig. 23F). Posterior part of fronto-clypeal apotome may have two pale areas (arrows, Fig. 22D).

Stony substratum in large streams and rivers. Widespread and common in northern and western Britain and in Ireland.

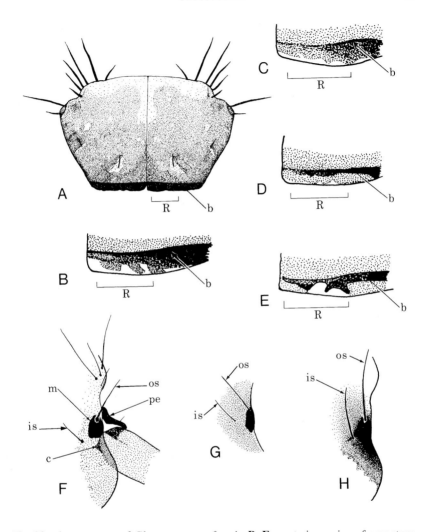

Fig. 23. **A:** pronotum of *Glossosoma conformis*. **B–E:** posterior region of pronotum, area of right side adjacent to the median suture: B, *G. conformis*; C, *G. intermedium*; D, E, *G. boltoni*. **F:** prothorax in region of articulation of pronotum with leg, dorso-lateral view, of *G. boltoni*. **G, H:** pronotum in region of articulation with leg, dorso-lateral view: G, *G. intermedium*; H, *G. conformis*.

4(1) 8th abdominal segment with posterior-lateral seta *ps* dark and conspicuous, larger than the small fine dorsal setae *fs* (Figs 20G,H, 24A); 3rd abdominal segment with prominent lateral seta *ls* (Fig. 24G)—   **Agapetus fuscipes** Curtis

Last two instars

Most specimens key out here. For additional features on pronotum, metadorsum and tarsal claw see the second parts of couplets 5 and 6.

Stony substratum; permanent streams of all sizes, rivers and lake-shores. Widespread and abundant.

—   8th abdominal segment with posterior-lateral seta *ps* pale and inconspicuous, similar in size to or smaller than the fine dorsal setae *fs* (Figs 24B,C); 3rd abdominal segment without prominent lateral seta (Fig. 24H)—   **5**

5   On the pronotum, that portion of the lateral mark *m* which is as dark as the posterior band *b*, extends more than half way between setal group *a* and seta *p* (Fig. 25A). Metadorsal sclerite *ts* has a maximum dimension which is less than half the distance between metadorsal setae *ta* and *tp* and less than the distance between mesodorsal setae *sa* and *sp* (Fig. 25D)—   **Agapetus delicatulus** McLachlan

Last two instars

8th abdominal segment with posterior-lateral seta *ps* pale and similar in size to the small, fine dorsal setae *fs* (Fig. 24B).

Stony substratum in large streams and rivers. Northern and western Britain and southern half of Ireland; common.

—   On the pronotum, that portion of the lateral mark *m* which is as dark as the posterior band *b* extends less than half way between setal group *a* and seta *p* (Figs 25B,C). Metadorsal sclerite *ts* has a maximum dimension which is at least half the distance between metadorsal setae *ta* and *tp* and at least as great as the distance between mesodorsal setae *sa* and *sp* (Figs 25E,F)—   **6**

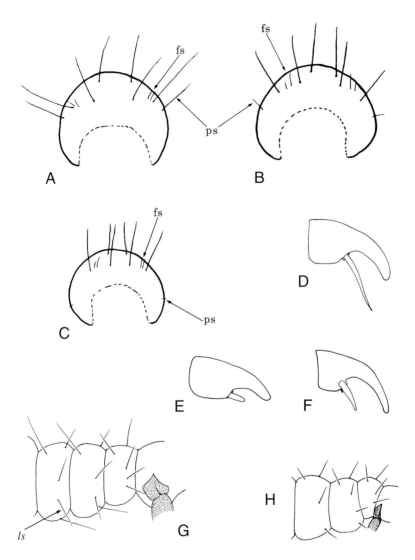

Fig. 24. **A–C:** 8th abdominal segment, posterior-dorsal view: A, *Agapetus fuscipes*; B, *A. delicatulus*; C, *A. ochripes*. **D–F**: tarsal claw: D, *A. fuscipes*; E, *A. fuscipes* (severely worn); F, *A. ochripes*. **G, H:** 1st, 2nd and 3rd abdominal segments, lateral view: G, *A. fuscipes*; H, *A. ochripes*.

6   Metadorsal sclerite *ts* has a maximum dimension which is about half the distance between metadorsal setae *ta* and *tp* and similar to the distance between mesodorsal setae *sa* and *sp* (Fig. 25E). Basal seta of tarsal claw without tapering flexuous tip, though it may be curved (Fig. 24F) (just after a moult the tip is flexuous but this soon wears away)—

Agapetus ochripes Curtis

Final instar

8th abdominal segment with posterior-lateral seta *ps* minute, not easily seen, much smaller than the fine dorsal setae *fs* (Fig. 24C).

Stony substratum; rivers, also streams in southern England. Widespread and common.

—   Metadorsal sclerite *ts* has a maximum dimension which is more than half (usually two-thirds) the distance between metadorsal setae *ta* and *tp* and much greater than the distance between mesodorsal setae *sa* and *sp* (Fig. 25F). Basal seta of tarsal claw with tapering flexuous tip (Fig. 24D), (unless claw is severely worn, as in Fig. 24E)—

Agapetus fuscipes Curtis

Last two instars

Specimens with missing or damaged posterior-lateral setae on the 3rd and 8th abdominal segments key out here.

See couplet 4 for habitat and distribution.

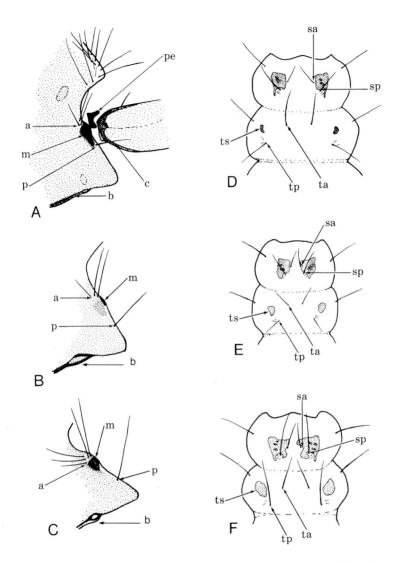

Fig. 25. **A:** prothorax in region of articulation of pronotum with leg, dorso-lateral view, of *Agapetus delicatulus*. **B, C:** pronotum in region of articulation with leg, dorso-lateral view: B, *A. ochripes*; C, *A. fuscipes*. **D–F:** mesodorsum and metadorsum: D, *A. delicatulus*: E, *A. ochripes*; F, *A. fuscipes*.

KEY TO FAMILY GOERIDAE
(TWO GENERA AND THREE SPECIES)

Larvae of the three goerid species (Table 4) are easily recognised by their characteristic mesopleurite, which is produced anteriorly as a finger-like process (*ap* in Figs 26C–F) projecting free from the body and extending forwards below the ventral edge of the pronotum. The anterior-lateral corners of the pronotum are also produced as pointed, forwardly-directed processes (Fig. 27E, p. 71). Anteriorly, the head narrows markedly and has a distinctly humped appearance when viewed from the side.

The rigid, well-ballasted cases of the Goeridae are characteristic, consisting of a strong tube of sand grains with larger rock fragments incorporated laterally (Fig. 26A). When the larva retracts into its case the head and sclerites of the first and second thoracic segments form a domed plug which effectively seals off the anterior opening of the case, as described and figured by Nielsen (1942). Larvae feed by scraping algae and other materials from surfaces; they have plain, toothless tips to the mandibles (resembling Figs 56C,E, p. 147) typical of this feeding method. Goerid larvae are particularly likely to be covered with a fine layer of sediment; this needs to be removed if it obscures important features.

The larvae are subject to parasitism by the ichneumon *Agriotypus armatus* Curtis, and it is not uncommon in some localities to find a pupal case with a long ribbon-like thread projecting from it (Fig. 26B). This is an extension of the cocoon of the contained parasite and is probably respiratory in function.

The flight period of all three goerids found in the British Isles extends from May to September. Final-instar larvae can be found at most seasons but are commonest in spring and early summer.

Table 4. Headwidths of Goeridae: ranges (mm) (and *n*) at instars II to V.

* Not keyed to species at this instar.

† Data from foreign material (Nielsen 1942).

Species	Instar II	Instar III	Instar IV	Instar V
Goera pilosa	0.29–0.32 (6)	0.48, 0.57 (2)	0.71–0.86 (4)	1.08–1.24 (15)
Silo nigricornis †	* 0.31–0.33	0.48–0.52	0.72–0.83	1.00–1.16
Silo pallipes	* 0.29 (1)	0.41–0.47 (7)	0.63–0.77 (38)	0.90–1.08 (13)

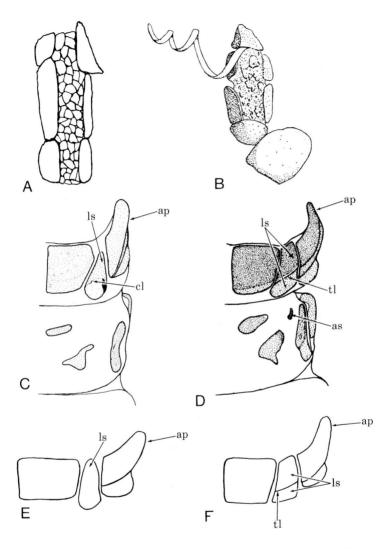

Fig. 26. **A:** case of *Silo pallipes*, dorsal view. **B:** pupal case of *Silo* sp. parasitised by *Agriotypus armatus*. **C, D:** mesothorax and metathorax, right half, dorsal view: C, *Goera pilosa*; D, *Silo nigricornis*. **E, F:** outlines of sclerites of mesothorax, right half, dorsal view: E, *G. pilosa*, instar II; F, *S. pallipes*, instar II.

KEY TO LARVAE

1   Mesonotal lateral sclerite *ls* with bluntly pointed apex (Figs 26C,E, p. 69); the sclerite is not divided into two by a transverse ecdysial line (though a curved brown line, *cl* in Fig. 26C, may mark off the polished posterior part of the sclerite from the remainder). Metadorsum without anterior-lateral sclerite (Fig. 26C). Fronto-clypeal apotome with bulbous posterior region (Fig. 27A)—   **Goera pilosa** (Fabricius)

In fast-flowing water in streams and rivers and on gravelly lake-shores. Widespread and common.

—   Mesonotal lateral sclerite *ls* with truncate apex (Figs 26D,F); sclerite is divided into two by a transverse ecdysial line *tl* * (Figs 26D,F). Metadorsum with anterior-lateral sclerite *as* * (Fig. 26D). Fronto-clypeal apotome with tapering posterior region (Fig. 27B)—   Genus SILO, **2**

* *Silo* species; asterisks denote characters that are NOT visible in some instar-II larvae (headwidth less than 0.38 mm).

2   Headwidth more than 0.38 mm—   **3**

—   Headwidth less than 0.38 mm—   **Silo nigricornis** (Pictet)
     Silo pallipes (Fabricius)
     Instar II

3   Posterior face of femur of 1st leg with additional setae *fs* on the proximal half (Fig. 27C). If headwidth is more than 0.60 mm, pronotum has 3 slightly raised areas (arrows, Fig. 27E) which are pale in contrast to the dark colour of the rest of the pronotum—   **Silo pallipes** (Fabricius)
     Instars III to V

Streams and rivers. Widespread and common.

—   Posterior face of femur of 1st leg without additional setae *fs* on the proximal half (though they are usually present on the distal half, Fig. 27D). Pronotum never with 3 pale areas, generally uniform in colour (Fig. 27F) or with a contrasting pale anterior margin in dark larvae—   **Silo nigricornis** (Pictet)
     Instars III to V

Streams and rivers. Common in south-east England, increasingly rarer further north; also recorded from Ireland.

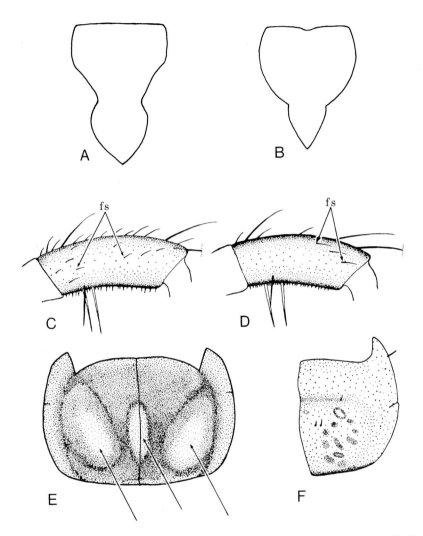

Fig. 27. **A, B:** fronto-clypeal apotome: A, *Goera pilosa*; B, *Silo nigricornis*. **C, D:** femur of 1st leg, posterior view: C, *S. pallipes*; D, *S. nigricornis*. **E:** pronotum of *S. pallipes*. **F:** pronotum, right half, of *S. nigricornis*.

KEY TO FAMILY HYDROPTILIDAE
(SEVEN GENERA AND THIRTY-ONE SPECIES)

Larvae of the family Hydroptilidae are very small, only 2.5 to 7.5 mm in length when fully grown. They are most likely to be encountered at the final instar (V), when the larva inhabits a distinctive, seed-like case (e.g. Figs 28E, 29A, 31D, 32B) which, in most genera, is strongly flattened laterally. At this stage the thoracic and 9th abdominal segments each bear a dorsal sclerotized plate.

The first four larval instars are caseless and differ markedly in form from the final instar. The anal proleg claws are long and slender and dorsal sclerites are present on the thoracic and all of the abdominal segments. Setae, and gills if present, are relatively long. On assuming the final instar, the dorsal sclerites are lost from abdominal segments 1 to 8, the conspicuous lateral fringe of setae is lost from the abdomen, there are changes in the proportions of the larva, and case-building commences. The enlargement of the abdomen during the final instar is very striking.

Found in all types of waterbody except small pools and temporary waters, the larvae feed on periphyton and fine organic particles. Some are specialised for feeding on filamentous algae (Wiggins 1977), the mouthparts being adapted for breaching the cell walls and sucking out the semi-fluid contents (Nielsen 1948). Disney (1972) has described larvae of *Orthotrichia* sp. sucking out the contents of pupae and eggs of *Simulium* in streams in Cameroon. Some species have two generations a year, overwintering as larvae or prepupae and flying in early summer; the offspring of this flight grow rapidly and adults appear from late summer.

Of the 31 known species of Hydroptilidae in Britain and Ireland, the larvae of only 21 have been described. The main published sources of information for these 21 species are listed below; asterisks denote sources that include information on the early instars.

Agraylea multipunctata: Nielsen (1948)*; Hickin (1967); Lepneva (1970); Solem (1972); Moretti (1983); Waringer & Graf (1997).
Agraylea sexmaculata: Lepneva (1970); Barnard (1971); Solem (1972); Moretti (1983); Waringer & Graf (1997).
Allotrichia pallicornis: Giudicelli & Vaillant (1967).
Hydroptila forcipata: Fahy (1971).
Hydroptila lotensis: Kachalova (1972), crude figure only.

Hydroptila pulchricornis: Lepneva (1970).

Hydroptila sparsa: Hanna (1961); Hickin (1967); Lepneva (1970); Moretti (1983).

Hydroptila tineoides: Nielsen (1948) *; Hickin (1967); Lepneva (1970), Moretti (1983).

Hydroptila vectis: Jacquemart & Coineau (1962); Lepneva (1970); Moretti (1983); Waringer & Graf (1997).

Ithytrichia ?clavata: Ross (1944); Wiggins (1977).

Ithytrichia lamellaris: Nielsen (1948) *; Hickin (1967); Lepneva (1970); Moretti (1983); Waringer & Graf (1997).

Orthotrichia angustella: Jacquemart (1962).

Orthotrichia costalis: Nielsen (1948) *; Hickin (1967); Lepneva (1970); Moretti (1983); Waringer & Graf (1997).

Orthotrichia tragetti: Moretti (1983).

Oxyethira distinctella: Lepneva (1970.

Oxyethira flavicornis: Nielsen (1948) *; Hickin (1967); Lepneva (1970); Moretti (1983); Waringer & Graf (1997).

Oxyethira frici: Lepneva (1970); Moretti (1983).

Oxyethira sagittifera: Siltala (1907)*; Lepneva (1970).

Oxyethira simplex: Macdonald (1950); Hickin (1967); Moretti (1983).

Oxyethira tristella: Lepneva (1970).

Tricholeiochiton fagesii: Lepneva (1970); Moretti (1983); Waringer & Graf (1997).

IMPORTANT NOTE. As a consequence of the variable detail of descriptions given in the above sources, and the lack of any information on the larvae of ten species, only four species (Table 5) can be identified with confidence. However, described generic characters appear to be constant enough to allow identification to that level. Some features are most easily seen when the whole animal is mounted in a fluid-filled cavity slide, illuminated by transmitted light, and examined using a monocular microscope at a magnification of x100.

Table 5. Headwidths of Hydroptilidae: ranges (mm) at instar V.

* British species that can be identified at instar V; † Data from foreign material (Nielsen 1948).

Species	Instar V	Species	Instar V
* *Agraylea multipunctata* †	0.31–0.38	*Ithytrichia lamellaris* †	0.27–0.33
* *Agraylea sexmaculata*	0.25–0.28	*Orthotrichia costalis* †	0.21–0.24
* *Allotrichia pallicornis*	0.32–0.38	*Oxyethira flavicornis* †	0.19–0.23
Hydroptila tineoides †	0.19–0.23	* *Tricholeichiton fagesii*	0.18

KEY TO LARVAE

1   Anal proleg claw long and slender, not sharply angled (Figs 28A,B).
     Abdominal segments 1–8 with dorsal sclerites (Fig. 28A). Larva
     caseless—   Instars II to IV

     These early instars are not separated here, but further information is given by
     Siltala (1907) and by Nielsen (1948) who also provides a key to all genera except
     Allotrichia and *Tricholeiochiton*.

—   Anal proleg claw short and thick, sharply angled (Figs 28C, 32A, p. 83).
     Abdominal segments 1–8 without dorsal sclerites (Figs 29E,F, p. 77).
     Larva case-bearing—   **2**

2   Most abdominal segments with dorsal and ventral ovoid processes (Fig.
     28D)—   Genus ITHYTRICHIA

     Case of secretion, oval in shape with a narrow anterior opening (Fig. 28E). Tibia
     of 1st leg without a ventral process (Fig. 28F), (unlike that of *Oxyethira*, a genus
     with a rather similar case; its ventral process is shown arrowed in Fig. 28G).

—   Abdominal segments without dorsal and ventral ovoid processes (e.g.
     Figs 29D, 30C, 31A)—   **3**

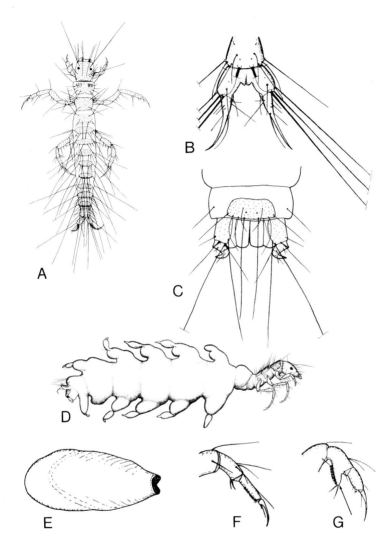

Fig. 28. **A:** instar III larva of *Agraylea multipunctata*, dorsal view. **B, C:** 9th abdominal segment, dorsal view, of *A. multipunctata*: B, instar IV; C, instar V. **D, E:** *Ithytrichia lamellaris*: D, larva, lateral view; E, case, lateral view. **F, G:** tibia and tarsus of 1st leg: F, *I. lamellaris*; G, *Oxyethira* sp.

3   Case not laterally compressed; there are two conspicuous ridges on each side of the mid-dorsal line (Figs 29A,B); case of secretion only. 2nd abdominal segment with lateral protuberances which extend anteriorly alongside the 1st abdominal segment (arrow, Fig. 29E). Labrum with a median sclerotized point (arrow, Fig. 29C); (it is usually necessary to detach the labrum in order to distinguish the point clearly from other mouthparts)—   Genus ORTHOTRICHIA

Abdomen with neither deep intersegmental constrictions nor folds across the segments (Figs 29D,E). Anal proleg claw without accessory hooks on its convex face (as in Fig. 32A, p. 83). 2nd and 3rd legs up to one-and-a-half times as long as 1st leg (Fig. 29D).

—   Case laterally compressed (Figs 30D,E, p. 79 and 31D,E, p. 81), without ridges on each side of the mid-dorsal line; case of minute mineral particles or of secretion with or without incorporated algal filaments. 2nd abdominal segment without lateral protuberances and not extending anteriorly alongside the 1st abdominal segment (Fig. 29F). Labrum without a median sclerotized point (Figs 32E,F, p. 83)—   **4**

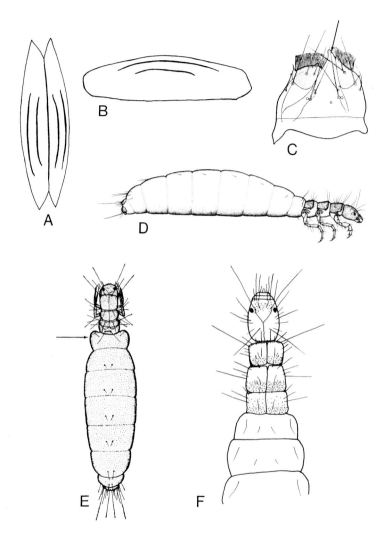

Fig. 29. **A, B:** case of *Orthotrichia costalis*: A, dorsal view; B, lateral view. **C:** labrum, dorsal view, of *O. costalis*. **D, E:** larva of *O. costalis*: D, lateral view; E, dorsal view. **F:** anterior part of larva of *Agraylea multipunctata*, dorsal view.

4   2nd and 3rd legs at least twice as long as 1st leg (Figs 30A,C).
     Abdominal segments without transverse folds (Figs 30A,C). Case of
     secretion only, without incorporated algal filaments or mineral particles
     (Figs 30B,D)—   5

—   2nd and 3rd legs up to one-and-a-half times as long as 1st leg (Figs 31A,
     p. 81, 32C, p. 83). Abdomen with transverse folds *f* across some
     segments (Figs 31A, 32C). Case of minute mineral particles or of
     secretion with incorporated algal filaments which may be transparent
     (Figs 31D, 32B,M)—   6

5   2nd and 3rd legs 4–5 times as long as 1st leg (Fig. 30A). Tibiae of 2nd
     and 3rd legs about twice as long as their respective tarsi (Fig. 30A). Case
     with anterior and posterior ends of similar shape (Fig. 30B)—
                                           Genus TRICHOLEIOCHITON

     Tricholeiochiton fagesii (Guinard) is the only species recorded in the British
     Isles.
     Weedy, still waters. Rare.

—   2nd and 3rd legs 2–3 times as long as 1st leg (Fig. 30C). Tibiae of 2nd
     and 3rd legs similar in length to their respective tarsi (Fig. 30C). Case
     with narrow anterior and broad posterior openings (Fig. 30D)—
                                           Genus OXYETHIRA

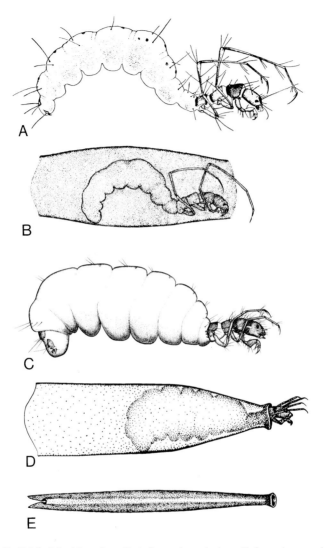

Fig. 30. **A, B:** *Tricholeiochiton fagesii*: A, larva, lateral view; B, larva in case, lateral view. **C–E:** *Oxyethira* sp.: C, larva, lateral view; D, larva in case, lateral view; E, case, ventral view.

6(4) Anal proleg with gill filament *g* (Figs 31A,B). Anal proleg claw with accessory hooks (arrows, Fig. 31C). Case of sand grains (Figs 31D,E). An uncommon and as yet unidentified *Hydroptila* makes a beautiful case entirely of closely aligned and abutted algal filaments (Fig. 31F)—

Genus HYDROPTILA

Case usually with the dorsal and ventral edges obviously of a different shape.

—   Anal proleg without gill filament. Anal proleg claw without accessory hooks (Fig. 32A, p. 83). Case of secretion usually with incorporated algal filaments (these may be transparent); the filaments are separated by secreted material (Figs 32B,M)—   7

Fig. 31. **A:** larva of *Hydroptila* sp., lateral view. **B, C:** *Hydroptila tineoides*: B, 9th abdominal segment, lateral view; C, left anal proleg claw, median view. **D–F:** *Hydroptila* sp.: D, larva in case, lateral view; E, case, ventral view; F, detail of case built from algal filaments.

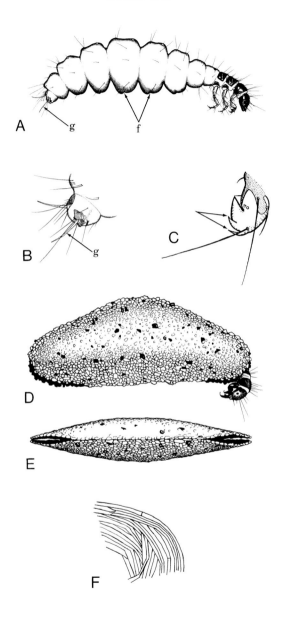

7   Mesonotum and metanotum with dark markings (Figs 29F, p. 77, 32D).
     Labrum with some very long setae (Figs 32D,E). Tarsi of 2nd and 3rd
     legs about twice as long as tarsus of 1st leg (Figs 32G–I). Tibiae of 2nd
     and 3rd legs without a ventral prominence (Figs 32H,I). In still or slow-
     flowing water—   Genus AGRAYLEA

     Two species of *Agraylea* have been recorded from the British Isles. **Agraylea
     sexmaculata** Curtis has a characteristic pattern of spots on the dorsal surface of
     the head and on the pronotum, mesonotum and metanotum (Fig. 32D); **Agraylea
     multipunctata** Curtis lacks dark spots but has a posterior band of colour on the
     mesonotum and metanotum and sometimes also on the head and pronotum (Figs
     29F, 32C). Stroot (1989) notes variation of patterning in *Agraylea multipunctata*.

     Both species occur in a wide variety of still and slowly–flowing waterbodies. *A.
     multipunctata* is widespread and common; *A. sexmaculata* is less frequent.

—   Mesonotum and metanotum uniformly pale, without dark markings.
     Labrum with short setae only (Fig. 32F). Tarsi of 2nd and 3rd legs
     similar in length to tarsus of 1st leg (Figs 32J–L). Tibiae of 2nd and 3rd
     legs each with a ventral prominence (arrows, Figs 32K,L). In fast-
     flowing water—   Genus ALLOTRICHIA

     Case with algal filaments loosely attached, giving the case a rough appearance,
     particularly if some of them become detached (Fig. 32M).

     Allotrichia pallicornis (Eaton) is the only species recorded in the British Isles.

     Streams and moderate to fast-flowing rivers; stony substratum. Widespread,
     locally common.

Fig. 32. **A–C:** *Agraylea multipunctata*: A, left anal proleg claw, lateral view; B, case,
     lateral view; C, larva, lateral view. **D:** head and thorax, dorsal view, of
     Agraylea sexmaculata. **E, F:** labrum, dorsal view: E, *A. multipunctata*; F, *A.
     pallicornis*. **G–I:** tibia and tarsus of *A. multipunctata*: G, 1st leg; H, 2nd leg;
     I, 3rd leg. **J–L:** tibia and tarsus of *A. pallicornis*: J, 1st leg; K, 2nd leg; L, 3rd
     leg. **M:** case of *Allotrichia pallicornis*.

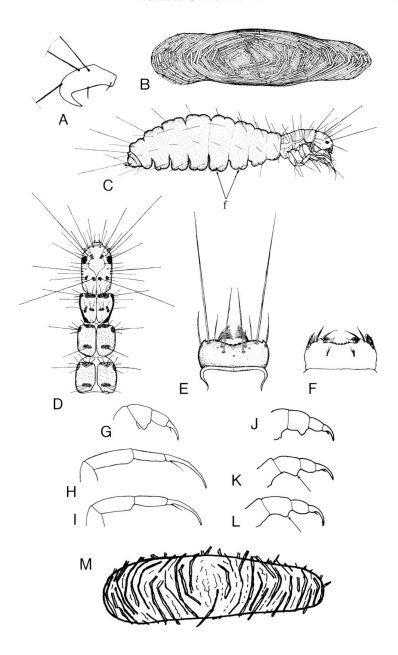

KEY TO FAMILY LEPIDOSTOMATIDAE
(THREE GENERA AND THREE SPECIES)

There are only three species of Lepidostomatidae (Table 6) in the British Isles. All are found in permanent, flowing water and one, *Lepidostoma hirtum*, also occurs on lake-shores. The larvae are small to medium in size and have brown heads, often with paler muscle attachment spots (Fig. 13D, p. 39). They are distinguished from all other caddis larvae except the limnephilids by the arrangement of the dorsal sclerites of the thorax (Fig. 33A, p. 87). Lepidostomatids differ from limnephilids by having a genal fold (*f*, Fig. 13E), by the position of the antennae, and by the absence of a dorsal protuberance on the first abdominal segment.

Early-instar larvae of all three species construct cases of sand grains and these remain the constructional medium for all *Lasiocephala basalis* and some larvae of the other two species. Usually, however, *Crunoecia irrorata* and *L. hirtum* change to plant material for case-building, arranging it to give a square cross-section and producing a two-part case of a type unique to this family (Fig. 33D). Eventually, some larvae end up with a case composed entirely of plant material (Fig. 33E), which resembles that of young *Brachycentrus subnubilus* (Fig. 19B, p. 51), the only other caddis to make a square-section case of plant material. *Lepidostoma hirtum* and *B. subnubilus* are often found together but the highly specialised legs of *B. subnubilus* easily distinguish it (Fig. 12A,B, p. 37).

Final-instar larvae can be found for many months of the year, as all three species have fairly long summer flight periods. *Crunoecia irrorata* and *L. hirtum* have been found over winter at instars II to V, *L. basalis* at instars IV and V. Larvae of *L. basalis* aggregate for pupation (Jenkins 1974), and are particularly associated with submerged wood (Hoffmann 2000).

Table 6. Headwidths of Lepidostomatidae: ranges (mm) (and *n*) for instars II to V.

*Not keyed to species at this instar.

Species	Instar II	Instar III	Instar IV	Instar V
Crunoecia irrorata	0.22 (2)	0.29–0.32 (7)	0.43–0.51 (26)	0.61–0.70 (20)
Lasiocephala basalis	*0.25–0.26 (13)	0.37–0.43 (22)	0.61–0.70 (30)	0.99–1.15 (34)
Lepidostoma hirtum	*0.20–0.25 (10)	0.32–0.38 (32)	0.54–0.61 (14)	0.84–1.01 (13)

KEY TO LARVAE

1 Posterior metadorsal sclerite *p* with 1 seta, resembling the anterior-median sclerite *a*, which also bears a single seta (Figs 33A,C, p. 87); (sclerites may be very pale in colour)— **2**

— Posterior metadorsal sclerite *p* with more than 1 seta (1 large and 2 small at instar II, at least 6 at instar V), unlike the anterior-median sclerite *a* which bears a single seta (Fig. 33B)— **Crunoecia irrorata** (Curtis)

Case initially circular in section, straight, made of sand grains; later, the larva usually changes to plant material for case construction, producing a case which is in part or entirely quadrangular in section (Fig. 33D).

Among dead leaves in shallow water of permanent trickles and oozes and at the margins of tiny woodland streams. Widespread and common.

2   Each side of mesonotum with several setae *as* on the anterior edge (3 to
     4 at instar III, many at instar V) in addition to the anterior-lateral group
     (Fig. 33C)—   **Lasiocephala basalis** (Kolenati)
                                                                    Instars III to V

     Case curved, made of sand grains (Fig. 33F).

     Occurs in a variety of flowing waters. Widespread but local in England, Wales
     and Ireland, rare in Scotland; often abundant where found.

—   Each side of mesonotum with only 1 seta *as* on the anterior edge in
     addition to the anterior-lateral group (Fig. 33A)—   **3**

3   Headwidth more than 0.3 mm—   **Lepidostoma hirtum** (Fabricius)
                                                                    Instars III to V

     Case initially of sand grains, but by instar V it is usually composed mainly or
     entirely of plant fragments arranged to give a square cross-section (as in Figs
     33D,E); occasionally, a larva does not change construction material and the
     instar V case of sand grains may be slightly curved.

     Rivers, large streams and sometimes on lake-shores. Widespread and common.

—   Headwidth less than 0.3 mm—   **Lasiocephala basalis** (Kolenati)
                                              Lepidostoma hirtum (Fabricius)
                                                                      Instar II

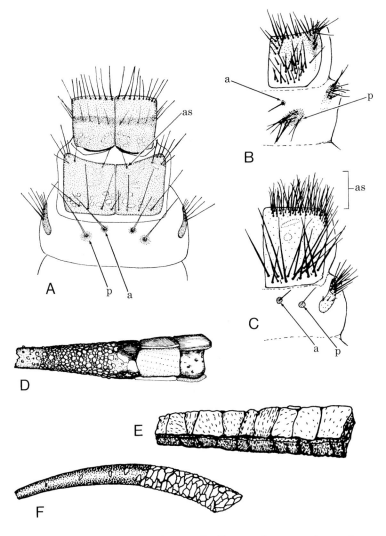

Fig. 33. **A:** thorax of *Lepidostoma hirtum*. **B, C:** mesodorsum and metadorsum, sclerites of right half: B, *Crunoecia irrorata*; C, *Lasiocephala basalis*. **D–F:** case: D, *C. irrorata*; E, *L. hirtum*; F, *L. basalis*.

KEY TO FAMILY LEPTOCERIDAE
(TEN GENERA AND THIRTY-ONE SPECIES)

Leptocerids are principally caddis of large waterbodies such as rivers and lakes. Final-instar larvae of most species are found for only a short period, usually during early and mid summer; they are small, most being 6 to 12 mm in length with headwidths of 0.5 to 1.0 mm when full-grown (Table 7). There are 31 species in the British Isles and the larvae show a considerable degree of morphological variation.

Compared with other cased caddis, most leptocerid larvae have very long antennae. The exceptions are late-instar sponge-eating *Ceraclea* larvae, which have short antennae protected by a lobe (Figs 43H,I, p. 111) and are distinguished from larvae of other families by the presence of dark posterior-lateral projections on the mesonotum. Final-instar leptocerids are characterised by the presence of an additional cleavage line on the head capsule, the subocular ecdysial line *sl* (Figs 35A, p. 93 and 40B,H, p. 103). Some species also have a supra-ocular ecdysial line, *xl* (Fig. 42G, p. 109). The additional lines distinguish the final instar without the need to measure headwidth, but are difficult to see in pale larvae.

Beraeodes minutus (Beraeidae) is very similar to leptocerids, not only in the length and position of the antennae, but also in the long hind legs and slender appearance. The larva (Figs 16A–C, p. 45), which is radically different from other beraeid larvae, can be distinguished from leptocerids by the mosaic pattern on the pronotum at the final instar (Fig. 35H) and at earlier instars by the numerous setae on the fronto-clypeal apotome (Fig. 35G); (these are pale and are most easily seen with the head in lateral view illuminated from below, or with top light against a dark background). At all instars, leptocerids are characterised by the division of the femora of the second and third legs into short proximal (*fp*) and longer distal (*fd*) sections (Figs 34A–C, p. 91). A trochanter to femur articulation typical of most other families is exemplified by *Potamophylax latipennis* (Fig. 34D). If the antennal character in couplet 8 of the Key to Families (p. 32) has caused any problems, then the femoral character will help to resolve them. Problems are most likely to have arisen with Molannidae, which have moderately long antennae, especially at early instars (Fig. 99E, p. 229), and superficially resemble leptocerids (Fig. 11H, p. 35). Molannids are further distinguished from leptocerids by the presence of a process on the tibia of the first leg (Fig. 11E) and the unusual form of the tarsal

Table 7. Headwidths of Leptoceridae: ranges (mm) (and *n*) at instars II to V.

*Not keyed to species at this instar. †Examined at this instar but not measured.

Species	Instar II	Instar III	Instar IV	Instar V
Adicella filicornis	—	—	0.34–0.39 (7)	0.49–0.51 (5)
Adicella reducta	—	0.25 (1)	0.37–0.41 (4)	0.54–0.66 (14)
Athripsodes albifrons	—	—	—	0.62–0.89 (73)
Athripsodes aterrimus	0.21(2)	0.29–0.33 (16)	0.44–0.51 (40)	0.63–0.87 (67)
Athripsodes bilineatus	—	—	—	0.60–0.73 (23)
Athripsodes cinereus	—	0.29–0.40 (19)	0.46–0.57 (34)	0.71–0.88 (93)
Athripsodes commutatus	—	—	—	0.63–0.79 (26)
Athripsodes albifrons/ bilineatus/ commutatus	*0.18 (1)	*0.26–0.29 (22)	*0.40–0.50 (51)	—
Ceraclea albimacula	†	0.29 (1)	0.45–0.55 (3)	0.82–1.01 (31)
Ceraclea annulicornis	0.18 (1)	0.26, 0.27 (2)	0.42–0.50 (17)	0.67–0.87 (81)
Ceraclea dissimilis	0.12–0.18 (34)	0.20–0.27 (31)	0.33–0.45 (31)	0.57–0.74 (71)
Ceraclea fulva	0.21 (2)	0.32–0.39 (5)	0.55–0.71 (5)	0.84–1.04 (22)
Ceraclea nigronervosa	0.21, 0.22 (2)	0.37–0.39 (5)	0.62–0.71 (11)	1.03–1.40 (86)
Ceraclea senilis	0.20–0.22 (3)	0.34–0.40 (7)	0.59–0.68 (11)	0.91–1.21 (33)
Erotesis baltica	—	—	0.35–0.40 (4)	0.56 (2)
Leptocerus interruptus	—	*0.16–0.18 (4)	0.23–0.24 (10)	0.37–0.44 (14)
Leptocerus lusitanicus	—	—	0.23 (1)	0.42–0.48 (20)
Leptocerus tineiformis	—	—	0.25–0.27 (5)	0.43–0.55 (31)
Mystacides azurea	—	0.23–0.27 (13)	0.33–0.40 (35)	0.55–0.65 (34)
Mystacides longicornis	0.18–0.19 (6)	0.27–0.30 (6)	0.41–0.49 (16)	0.60–0.77 (16)
Mystacides nigra	—	0.25, 0.29 (2)	0.39–0.43 (11)	0.56–0.69 (14)
Oecetis furva	—	—	0.65, 0.69 (2)	0.83–1.07 (17)
Oecetis lacustris	—	0.28–0.29 (3)	0.41–0.49 (5)	0.71–0.88 (12)
Oecetis notata	—	—	0.43–0.49 (7)	0.77–0.87 (16)
Oecetis ochracea	—	0.39, 0.43 (2)	0.71–0.83 (15)	1.06–1.28 (16)
Oecetis testacea	—	—	0.41–0.46 (5)	0.67–0.76 (38)
Setodes argentipunctellus	0.12–0.13 (10)	0.17–0.21 (18)	0.23–0.29 (17)	0.37–0.41 (28)
Setodes punctatus	—	—	0.29 (2)	0.39–0.46 (5)
Triaenodes bicolor	0.18–0.22 (11)	0.28–0.34 (25)	0.39–0.48 (39)	0.59–0.88 (61)
Ylodes conspersus	*0.18, 0.21 (2)	*0.27–0.32 (8)	0.39–0.49 (14)	0.71–0.82 (22)
Ylodes reuteri	—	—	—	0.67–0.87 (6)
Ylodes simulans	—	—	*0.35–0.41 (9)	0.51–0.69 (43)

claw of the third leg (Fig. 11G). Larvae of Odontoceridae, Beraeidae and Sericostomatidae (which, like leptocerids, have the antennae close to the anterior margin of the head capsule) have articulations that could be confused with those of Leptoceridae. In *Odontocerum albicorne* the femur has a dark-coloured proximal tip (Fig. 34E) but is all one segment. In Beraeidae and Sericostomatidae the articulation is pale in colour and structures are difficult to distinguish, but a line marking off the proximal end of the femur can be seen easily in *Beraeodes minutus* (Fig. 34F) and with difficulty in the other species (Figs 34G,H). However, unlike leptocerids, there does not appear to be a separate sclerite in these families.

The third legs are much longer than the others and in some genera the tibia (and the tarsus in *Mystacides*) has a central constriction and pale band (*c*, Fig 34C). This feature, which is also present in Molannidae, allows slight flexion of the segment. A few species of leptocerids have setal fringes on the third legs (Figs 35E,F, p. 93) which enable the larva to swim well with its case by rapidly rowing the legs. No other cased caddis can swim so proficiently. Also unusual among cased caddis are the long, single-bladed jaws of *Oecetis*, used to capture worms and chironomid larvae which are swallowed whole.

The leptocerid pupal case has a single posterior opening through which the moulted larval sclerites are vigorously ejected; this may be done to prevent damage to the antennae, which are coiled round the posterior end of the pupa. Pupal cases are therefore less useful for identification than those of other families, where many of the sclerites are trapped by a grille or restricted opening. However, the cases of many species are characteristic and enable identification to be made through their shape and material used in manufacture.

Before using the key it is important to be familiar with the following features which are used in a number of couplets, sometimes without specific illustration.

Setal arrangement on the mesoventer and metaventer and 1st abdominal venter (Figs 35C,D, p. 93). Setal counts are usually quoted as 'on each side' of the mid-line. Sometimes, however, the two setal groups merge to give a continuous band and in such cases total numbers are quoted. It is always important to exclude from counts the seta *ps*, associated with each pleurite, and the seta *ls*, associated with each lateral sclerite on the 1st abdominal segment.

Protrochantin. This is fairly large in the leptocerids; its location is shown as *pt* in Fig. 35B (p. 93).

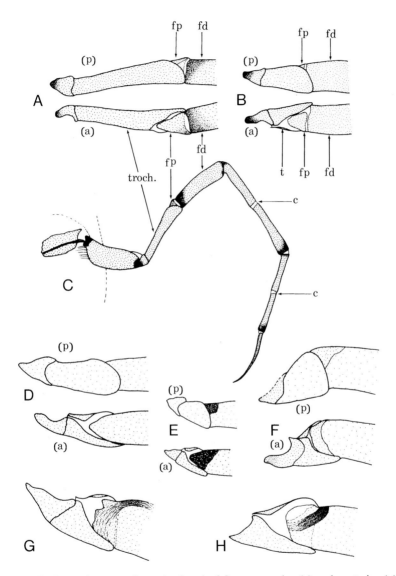

Fig. 34. **A, B:** trochanter and proximal end of femur, anterior (a) and posterior (p) views: A, 3rd leg of *Mystacides longicornis*; B, 2nd leg of *Ceraclea annulicornis*. C: metapleurite and 3rd leg, posterior view, of *M. longicornis*. **D–F:** trochanter and proximal end of femur of 3rd leg, anterior (a) and posterior (p) views: D, *Potamophylax latipennis*; E, *Odontocerum albicorne*; F, *Beraeodes minutus*. **G, H:** trochanter and proximal end of femur, anterior view, of *Sericostoma personatum*: G, 2nd leg; H, 3rd leg.

KEY TO LARVAE

(i)   Fronto-clypeal apotome with numerous down-pointing pale setae * (Fig.
       35G)—   **Beraeodes minutus** (L.)
                                                      (Family BERAEIDAE, p. 44)

       * It may be necessary, particularly at early instars, to view the head laterally
       against transmitted light to see these setae.

       Although *B. minutus* is not known at instars II and III, it is figured at instar I by
       Morton (1890); the general appearance of this first-instar larva closely resembles
       later instars so it is likely that the characteristic setae are present at instars II and
       III, but in reduced numbers.

       Pronotum with a dark mosaic pattern most obvious at instar V (Fig. 35H).

—   Fronto-clypeal apotome with only 10 setae—
                                                      Family LEPTOCERIDAE, 1

       Pronotum never with a mosaic pattern though it may have colour patches.

1   Tarsal claw *c* of 2nd leg hook-shaped (Fig. 36A, p. 95)—
                                                      Genus LEPTOCERUS, 2

       Leptocerus species are not separable at instars II and III: headwidth less than
       0.20 mm.

       3rd leg always with long anterior and posterior setal fringes (arranged as in Figs
       35E,F) which enable the larva to swim.

—   Tarsal claw *c* of 2nd leg curved but never hook-shaped (Fig. 38A, p.
       99)—   **4**

       In a few species, the 3rd leg has long setal fringes (Figs 35E,F; (a) and (p)
       respectively indicate anterior and posterior aspects of the leg) which enable the
       larva to swim.

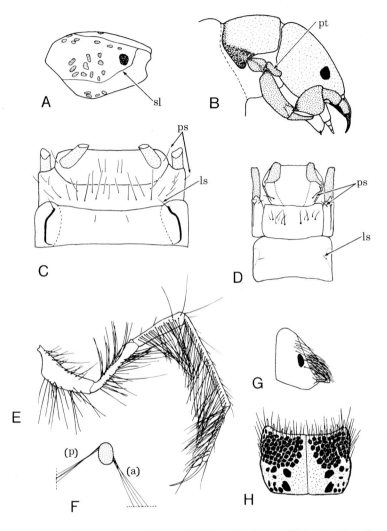

Fig. 35. **A:** head capsule, lateral view, of *Athripsodes cinereus*. **B:** head and prothorax, lateral view, of *Mystacides longicornis*. **C, D:** mesothorax, metathorax and 1st abdominal segment, ventral view: C, *Ceraclea fulva*; D, *Leptocerus tineiformis*. **E, F:** 3rd leg of *Triaenodes bicolor*: E, posterior view; F, diagrammatic transverse section of tibia. **G, H:** *Beraeodes minutus* (Beraeidae): G, head capsule, lateral view, instar IV; H, pronotum, instar V.

2   Distal part of anal proleg with 5 long setae AND a number of small setae
     ps (Fig. 36B); (avoid confusion with setae on the basal lobes, *ls* in Figs
     36B,C). Metadorsum with 1 long and 10 or more short anterior-lateral
     setae. Case almost straight, made from translucent, secreted material
     (Fig. 36F)—   **Leptocerus tineiformis** Curtis
                                                           Instars IV and V

     Lakes, large weedy ponds and occasionally canals. Mainly midland and southern
     England; absent from Scotland and Ireland.

—   Distal part of anal proleg with 5 long setae only (Fig. 36C). Metadorsum
     with only 1 anterior-lateral seta *al* (Fig. 36D). Case curved, made from
     secreted material with numerous embedded sand grains, at least in the
     posterior half (Fig. 36G)—   **3**

3   Mesonotum (Fig. 1. p. 15) central area with 2 or 3 setae *cs* (Fig. 36D).
     Metaventer (see Fig. 3, p. 17 and p. 90) with several setae on each side
     (as in Fig. 35D). Protrochantin central region pale (Fig. 36H) and similar
     in colour to the central area of the face of the 1st leg coxa—
                                             Leptocerus interruptus (Fabricius)
                                                           Instars IV and V

     Among vegetation, including tree roots, in slow-flowing regions of rivers.
     Records from Devon, Somerset, Herefordshire, Worcestershire and
     Monmouthshire.

—   Mesonotum central area with 7 to 12 setae *cs* (Fig. 36E). Metaventer
     with only 1 seta on each side. Protrochantin central region dark (Fig.
     36I), contrasting with the central area of the face of the 1st leg coxa—
                                             Leptocerus lusitanicus (McLachlan)
                                                           Instars IV and V

     South-east England in a few large rivers and nearby gravel pits. Among
     submerged vegetation and *Salix* roots.

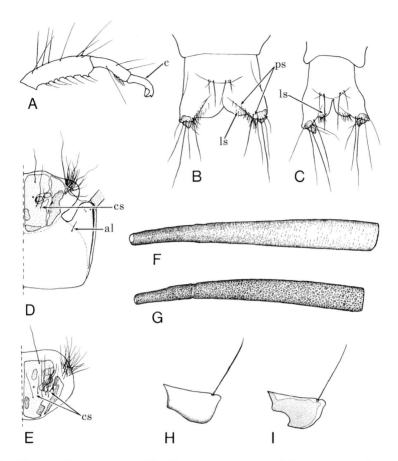

Fig. 36. **A:** tibia and tarsus of 2nd leg, posterior view, of *Leptocerus tineiformis*. **B, C:** 9th abdominal segment, dorsal view: B, *L. tineiformis*; C, *L. interruptus*. **D:** mesodorsum and metadorsum, right half, of *L. interruptus*. **E:** mesodorsum, right half, of *L. lusitanicus*. **F, G:** case: F, *L. tineiformis*; G, *L. lusitanicus*. **H, I:** protrochantin: H, *L. interruptus*; I, *L. lusitanicus*.

4(1) Mandibles about three times as long as their width at the base (Figs
      37B,D) and with only one cutting edge (Fig. 37B). Labrum with
      numerous setae on the dorsal surface (Fig. 37C)— Genus OECETIS, **5**

      Oecetis species are not separable at instar II: headwidth less than 0.25
      mm.

—   Mandibles at most twice as long as their width at the base and with two
      cutting edges, one dorsal and one ventral (Fig. 37A). Labrum with few
      setae on the dorsal surface (Figs 41A,B, p. 105)—   **9**

5   Mesoventer with 1–4 setae on each side; metaventer with a total of
      17–60 setae. Tarsal claw of 2nd and 3rd legs with a rudimentary basal
      seta (arrow, Fig. 37E)—   **6**

—   Mesoventer without setae; metaventer with only 1–6 setae. Tarsal claw
      of 2nd and 3rd legs with a prominent basal seta (arrow, Fig. 37F)—   **7**

6   Protrochantin with several long dark setae (Fig. 37G). 9th abdominal
      dorsum with 12 setae (Fig. 37J)—   **Oecetis lacustris** (Pictet)
                                                              Instars III to V

      Case curved and tapering, composed of sand grains.

      Lakes, large ponds, canals and slow-flowing rivers; muddy sand substrata and
      among tree roots. Widespread.

—   Protrochantin with only one long dark seta (Fig. 37H). 9th abdominal
      dorsum with more than 12 setae (up to 40 at instar V, Fig. 37K)—
                                                  Oecetis ochracea (Curtis)
                                                              Instars III to V

      Case curved, smooth, composed of sand grains, other small particles or a mixture
      of the two; very fragile compared with other caddis cases.

      Lakes, large ponds and canals; muddy and sandy substrata, often under several
      metres of water. Early coloniser of new reservoirs and lakes. Widespread and
      common.

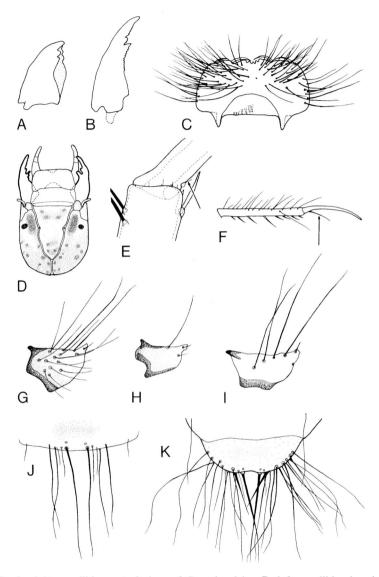

Fig. 37. **A:** right mandible, ventral view, of *Ceraclea fulva*. **B:** left mandible, dorsal view, of *Oecetis furva*. **C:** labrum, dorsal view of *O. ochracea*. **D:** head of *O. ochracea*. **E, F:** 3rd leg, posterior view: E, articular region of tarsus and claw of *O. ochracea*; F, tarsus and claw of *O. furva*. **G–I:** protrochantin: G, *O. lacustris*; H, *O. ochracea*; I, *O. notata*. **J, K:** part of 9th abdominal dorsum: J, *O. lacustris*; K, *O. ochracea*.

7(5) *Note: Separation has not been tested at instar III (headwidth less than 0.40 mm)*. Head and thoracic dorsal sclerites of a very pale straw colour, entirely lacking coloured patches or colour associated with muscle attachment spots. Protrochantin with more than 1 long dark seta (4 present at instar V, Fig. 37I)—   **Oecetis notata** (Rambur)
                                                                Instars IV and V

3rd legs with two long setal fringes (resembling Figs 35E,F, p. 93) which enable the larva to swim; this it does only reluctantly. Case dorso-ventrally flattened, composed of moss leaves.

In moderately-flowing regions of large rivers; moss-covered stones, tree roots. Recent records from South Wales, Herefordshire, south-west England, Ireland, and old records from south-east England.

— Head and thoracic dorsal sclerites with coloured patches and colour associated with muscle attachment spots (Fig. 38B). Protrochantin with only 1 long dark seta (as in Fig. 37H)—   **8**

8 *Note: Separation has not been tested at instar III (headwidth less than 0.40 mm)*. 3rd leg with 2 long setal fringes, most easily seen on the tibia (resembling Figs 35E,F, p. 93). Posterior dorsal margin of head with 3 pale muscle attachment spots on each side of the coronal suture (arrows, Fig. 38D). Larval case robust, with a flattened ventral face, and made of pieces of plant material, particularly roots (Figs 38F,G). 8th abdominal dorsum with all setae much shorter than those of the 9th abdominal dorsum—   **Oecetis testacea** (Curtis)
                                                                Instars IV and V

Larva may swim if disturbed.

Lake-shores, rivers and canals; most numerous among stones under plants. Widespread and locally common but apparently absent from eastern England.

— 3rd leg without long setal fringes (Fig. 38A). Posterior dorsal margin of head with 2 pale muscle attachment spots on each side of the coronal suture (arrows, Fig. 38C). Larval case fragile, not flattened, made from plant fragments (Fig. 38E). 8th abdominal dorsum with 1 long seta on each side which is about the size of the longer setae of the 9th abdominal dorsum—   **Oecetis furva** (Rambur)
                                                                Instars IV and V

Lakes and large ponds; among marginal plants. Widespread but local.

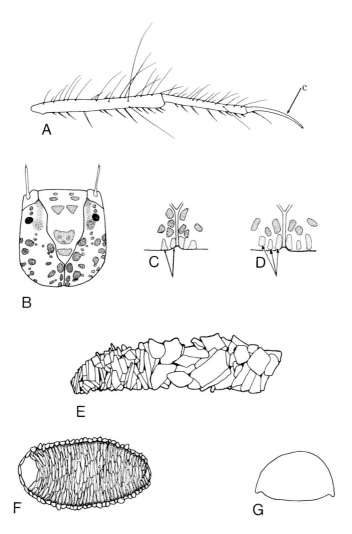

Fig. 38. **A:** tibia and tarsus of 3rd leg, posterior view, of *Oecetis furva*. **B:** head capsule of *O. furva*. **C, D:** posterior region of head adjacent to coronal suture: C, *O. furva*; D, *O. testacea*. **E:** case of *O. furva*. **F, G:** case of *O. testacea*: F, ventral view; G, outline of transverse section.

9(4) Mesonotum with posterior-lateral projections which are usually very dark in colour (arrows, Fig. 39A); (these may be hidden in the intersegmental fold). At least at instar V, most gills consist of several filaments—   **10**

— Mesonotum without posterior-lateral projections. If gills are present each consists of a single unbranched filament—
                    Genera ADICELLA, EROTESIS, MYSTACIDES,
                    SETODES, TRIAENODES, YLODES, **28**

10 Ventral apotome (arrow, Fig 39B) is triangular; even in small larvae the triangle is taller than its width at base (Fig. 39C). Gills never present on abdominal segments 4 to 8. Case without an overhanging dorsal lip (Figs 39F, G); composed of sand grains—   Genus ATHRIPSODES, **11**

— Ventral apotome (arrow, Fig. 39D) is quadrangular or polygonal; small larvae may have a triangular apotome but, if so, it is shorter than its width at base and has a rounded apex (Fig. 39C). Gills may be present on abdominal segments 4 to 8. Case with an overhanging dorsal lip (Figs 39H,I); composed of sand grains, secretion or a mixture of the two—
                                          Genus CERACLEA, **17**

11 Anterior face of trochanter and proximal part of distal section of femur of 3rd leg with many short dagger-shaped orange or straw-coloured setae (*ds* in Figs 39J,K; avoid confusion with spinule combs *sc*)—
                                  Athripsodes aterrimus (Stephens)

Ventral side of head, including apotome, generally pale in colour. Dark muscle attachment spots apparent in dorsal, lateral and ventral views of the head (Figs 39B, 40A) and on the pronotum and mesonotum (Fig. 39A). 9th abdominal dorsal sclerite and lateral sclerite of the anal proleg dark brown.

Ponds, lakes and slow-flowing waters, also faster-flowing water of lake outlets and below weirs; usually among plants and on muddy sand. Widespread and common.

— Anterior face of trochanter and femur of 3rd leg without any short dagger-shaped setae; setae present on these parts have long tapering tips, and many are brown in colour—   **12**

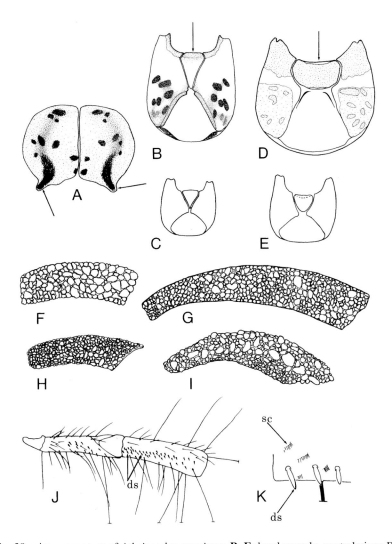

Fig. 39. **A:** mesonotum of *Athripsodes aterrimus*. **B–E:** head capsule, ventral view: B, *A. aterrimus*; C, *A. ?albifrons*, instar II; D, *Ceraclea senilis;* E, *C. senilis,* instar II. **F–I:** case: F, *A. ?albifrons*, instar II; G, *A. albifrons*; H, *C. dissimilis*, instar II; I, *C. annulicornis*. **J:** trochanter and femur of 3rd leg, anterior view, of *A. aterrimus*. **K:** proximo-ventral region of distal section of femur of 3rd leg, anterior view, of *A. aterrimus*, instar II.

12   Ventral edge of tibia of 1st leg with 1 or 2 setae in addition to the single
      seta *ts* at the distal end (Figs 40D,E; beware confusion with large
      spines)—   **Athripsodes cinereus** (Curtis)
                                                              Instars IV and V

      Ventral apotome and adjacent parts of the head very dark brown or black (Fig.
      40C). Lateral part of the head with distinct dark muscle attachment spots which
      are almost equivalent in intensity to those on the fronto-clypeal apotome and
      alongside the fronto-clypeal suture (Figs 35A, p. 93, 40B); (these spots are not
      visible in a melanic form fairly common in Mochrum Loch, Dumfries &
      Galloway).

      Rivers, streams, lakes and canals; stony and sandy substrata. Widespread and
      common.

—   Ventral edge of tibia of 1st leg with only a single seta *ts*, which is at the
      distal end (Fig. 40F)—   **13**

13   Subocular ecdysial line *sl* (Figs 35A, 40B) makes a pale gap in the
      darkly-coloured posterior ridge of the head capsule (Fig. 40H)—   **14**

—   No subocular ecdysial line or pale gap in the darkly-coloured posterior
      ridge of the head capsule; (ridge may be narrowed at a similar position,
      n in Fig. 40G)—   **16**

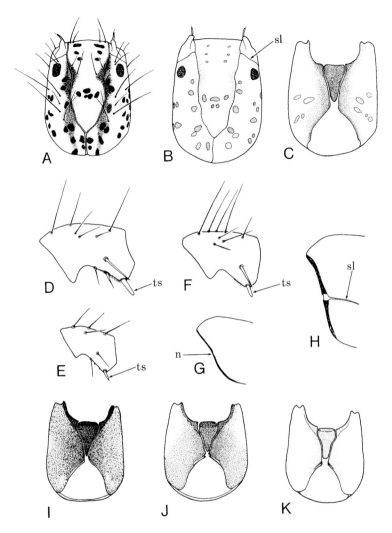

Fig. 40. **A:** head capsule of *Athripsodes aterrimus*. **B, C:** head capsule of *A. cinereus*; B, dorsal view; C, ventral view. **D–F:** tibia of 1st leg, anterior view: D, *A. cinereus*; E, *A. cinereus*, instar IV; F, *A. bilineatus*. **G, H:** posterior part of head capsule, lateral view, of *A. bilineatus*: G, instar IV; H, instar V. **I–K:** head capsule, ventral view: I, *A. bilineatus*; J, *A. albifrons*; K, *A. commutatus*.

14 The dark purse-shaped mark *m* in the middle of the anterior part of the labrum usually lies clear of the median pit *p* (Figs 41A,C); if the two abut, the posterior margin of the mark is not inflexed at that point (Fig. 41D); (this feature is best seen on a detached labrum using transmitted light) —   **Athripsodes bilineatus** (L.)

Instar V

Stony substratum; large streams and rivers throughout Britain, also small streams in south-east England and lake-shores in Scotland. Most frequent in northern and western Britain, rare in Ireland.

NOTE: A small proportion (less than 5%) of *A. albifrons* and *A. commutatus* key out here. They will not comply with at least one of the following characters. Metadorsum with the outer setae of the median quartet *q* over half the length of the inner pair (usually at least three-quarters, as shown in Fig. 41L). Muscle attachment spots *fp* on the posterior part of the frontoclypeal apotome are equivalent in intensity to those *lp* on the parietals bordering the fronto-clypeal suture (Fig. 41N); the lateral spots *lp* may merge with a band of colour. Ventral apotome with a pointed apex (Fig. 40I, p. 103).

— The purse-shaped mark *m* in the middle of the anterior part of the labrum has its posterior margin deeply invaginated around the median pit *p* (Fig. 41B); occasionally the margin apparently overlaps the pits (Figs 41E–J) or the two abut, in which case the margin is inflexed at that point (Fig. 41K) —   **15**

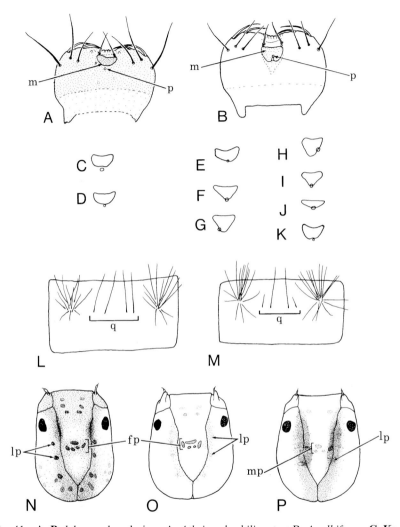

Fig. 41. **A, B:** labrum, dorsal view: A, *Athripsodes bilineatus*; B, *A. albifrons*. **C–K:** various arrangements of the purse-shaped mark and median pit of the labrum: C, D, *A. bilineatus*; E–G, *A. commutatus*; H–K, *A. albifrons*. **L, M:** metadorsum: L, *A. bilineatus*; M, *A. albifrons*. **N–P:** head capsule: N, *A. bilineatus*; O, *A. commutatus*; P, *A. albifrons*.

15 Metadorsum with the outer setae of the median quartet q less than half the length of the inner pair (usually one-third, as shown in Fig. 41M, p. 105). Median muscle attachment spots mp on the posterior part of the fronto-clypeal apotome are definitely paler than those lp on the parietals bordering the fronto-clypeal suture (Fig. 41P); the lateral spots lp may merge with a band of colour. Ventral apotome with pointed apex (Fig. 40J, p. 103)—   **Athripsodes albifrons** (L.)
Instar V

A small proportion of larvae will conform to only two of the three characters given above.

Stony substratum. Common in rivers everywhere except highland Scotland where it is very local; also on lake-shores in Ireland.

— Metadorsum with the outer setae of the median quartet q over half the length of the inner pair (usually two-thirds). Muscle attachment spots fp on the posterior part of the fronto-clypeal apotome are definitely darker than those lp on the parietals bordering the fronto-clypeal suture (Fig. 41O); (in very pale individuals the lateral spots lp are absent); the band of colour running adjacent to the fronto-clypeal suture, if apparent, is extremely pale. Ventral apotome with rounded apex (Fig. 40K)—
Athripsodes commutatus (Rostock)
Instar V

A small proportion of larvae will conform to only two of the three characters given above.

Stony substratum; rivers. Common in Scotland and Ireland; very local in northern England, southern Wales and south-west England; old isolated records of adults from elsewhere.

16(13) *Note: Separation has not been tested at instar II (headwidth less than 0.25 mm).* Muscle attachment spots that are clearly darker than the surrounding cuticle can be seen on the mesonotum, pronotum and lateral parts of the head capsule. No coloured bands on the parietals adjacent to the fronto-clypeal suture —   **Athripsodes cinereus** (Curtis)
                                                                   Instar III

Rivers, streams, lakes and canals; stony and sandy substrata. Widespread and common.

—   Muscle attachment spots not visible on the mesonotum; spots on the pronotum and lateral parts of the head capsule, if present, are irregular and very pale. There may be a brown band on the parietals adjacent to the fronto-clypeal suture (as in Fig. 41P, p. 105) —
                                              Athripsodes albifrons (L.)
                                              Athripsodes bilineatus (L.)
                                       Athripsodes commutatus (Rostock)
                                                   Instars III and IV *

* At instar IV (headwidth 0.40–0.50 mm) the head pattern differences described for instar V in couplets 14 and 15 are apparent in many specimens, though less clear. This will enable many to be identified; other characters available to separate larvae at instar V are unreliable for instars III and IV.

17(10) 3rd leg with two long setal fringes (Fig. 42A, arranged as in Fig. 42B, where (p) indicates the posterior aspect); larva may swim. Very small larva, headwidth around 0.2 mm and case length less than 2.5 mm—
Genus CERACLEA, Instar II, **23**

— 3rd leg without two long setal fringes (Figs 42C,D); larva does not swim. Larger larva—   Genus CERACLEA, Instars III to V, **18**

18 Mesoventer with setae (Fig. 35C, p. 93)—   **19**

— Mesoventer without setae—   **20**

19 Mesoventer with 1 seta on each side. Pronotum generally brown, without a very dark band along the anterior edge (Fig. 42E). Head brown with a pattern of dark muscle attachment spots (Fig. 42G). Protrochantin covered with prominent spinules (Figs 43A,B, p. 111) and with distal end *d* prolonged at instars IV and V (Fig. 43A; headwidth more than 0.50 mm). Anal proleg claw with 1 accessory hook (arrow, Figs 44C,D, p. 113)—   **Ceraclea senilis** (Burmeister)
Instars III to V

Case made with translucent, flexible secreted material and sponge spicules; living pieces of sponge are sometimes attached to the outside of the case.

Still or slow-flowing water; in sponges. Ireland, midland and southern England, Dumfries & Galloway; local.

— Mesoventer with 2 or more setae on each side (Fig. 35C). Pronotum pale with a distinctive very dark band along the anterior edge (Fig. 42F). Head pale, without a distinct colour pattern (Fig. 42H). Protrochantin with neither prominent spinules nor a prolonged distal end (as in Fig. 43C). Anal proleg claw with 2 accessory hooks (as in Figs 44A,B)—
Ceraclea fulva (Rambur)
Instars III to V

Case made with translucent, flexible secreted material and sponge spicules, frequently with living pieces of sponge attached to the outside (Fig. 44I).

Large ponds and lakes; in sponges. Widespread; common except in south-east England.

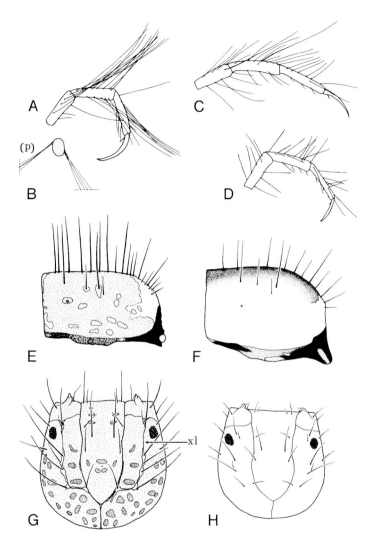

Fig. 42. **A, C, D:** femur, tibia and tarsus of 3rd leg, posterior view, of *Ceraclea dissimilis*: A, instar II; C, instar III; D, instar V. **B:** diagrammatic transverse section of tibia of 3rd leg of *C. dissimilis*, instar II. **E, F:** pronotum, right half: E, *C. senilis*; F, *C. fulva*. **G, H:** head capsule: G, *C. senilis*; H, *C. fulva*.

20(18) Metaventer with 2 or more setae on each side—   **21**

—   Metaventer with only 1 seta on each side—   **22**

21   Case composed of closely abutted sand grains (Fig. 43D), occasionally
        with roots incorporated at the anterior end. 9th abdominal dorsum with
        two groups of 3 setae (arrows, Fig. 43F), all smaller than the innermost
        setae *ps* of the anal proleg lateral sclerites (Fig. 43F). Rarely found in
        sponges—   **Ceraclea dissimilis** (Stephens)
                                                              Instars III to V

> Head pale in colour at all instars. Anal proleg claw with two accessory hooks (as
> in Figs 44A,B, p. 113).

> Rivers, large streams and stony lake-shores; on and under big stones, also on
> submerged tree roots but only in slow-flowing water. Widespread and common.

—   Case composed of tough, flexible secreted material with bands of
        embedded sand grains (Fig. 43E). 9th abdominal dorsum with two
        groups of 4 setae (arrows, Fig. 43G) each having at least 1 seta as long
        as the innermost setae *ps* of the anal proleg lateral sclerites (Fig. 43G).
        Usually associated with sponges—   **Ceraclea nigronervosa** (Retzius)
                                                              Instars III to V

> Instar V head with a distinctive pattern of dark brown patches (Fig. 43H);
> younger larvae have pale heads (Fig. 43I). Anal proleg claw with 1 or 2
> accessory hooks.

> Streams, rivers and lakes; stony substratum. Widespread and common.
> Overwinters as fully grown larva in pupal case.

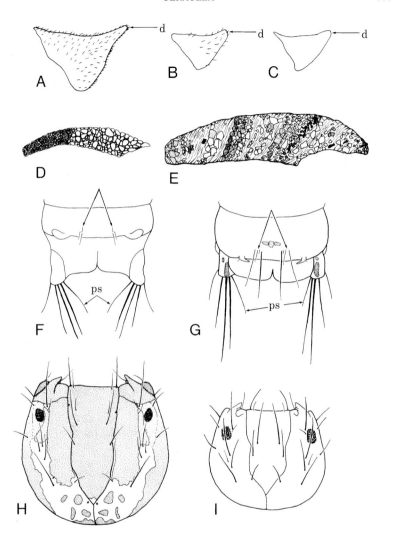

Fig. 43. **A–C:** protrochantin: A, *Ceraclea senilis*; **B, C:** *C. senilis*, instar III; C, *C. nigronervosa*. **D, E:** case: D, *C. dissimilis*, instar III; E, *C. nigronervosa*. **F, G:** 9th abdominal segment, dorsal view: F, *C. dissimilis*; G, *C. nigronervosa*. **H, I:** head capsule of *C. nigronervosa*: H, instar V; I, instar IV.

22(20) Case *EITHER* composed entirely of translucent, flexible secreted material without embedded sand grains (but sometimes with added pieces of sponge, as in Fig. 44I), *OR* (at instar III only) with a posterior end of closely abutted sand grains and an anterior end of secretion (Fig. 44H). Metadorsum with up to 3 setae in each anterior-lateral group *al*, at least one of which is longer than the median setae *m* (Fig. 44E). Anal proleg claw with 2 accessory hooks (arrows, Figs 44A,B). In sponges—
Ceraclea albimacula (Rambur)
Instars III to V

Head pale with faint muscle attachment spots at all instars. Tibia of 2nd leg without short setae on the ventral edge.

Rivers, large streams and canals. Widespread. Overwinters at instar II (but not necessarily in sponges).

—   Case always composed entirely of closely abutted sand grains (Fig. 39I, p. 101). Metadorsum with more than 3 setae in each anterior-lateral group *al* (6–12 at instar V, Fig. 44G), the longest of which are comparable with the median setae *m* (Fig. 44G). Anal proleg claw with 1 accessory hook (as in Figs 44C,D). Not found in sponges—
Ceraclea annulicornis (Stephens)
Instars III to V

Head reddish-orange at instar V, pale at earlier instars. Tibia of 2nd leg with 1–3 short setae on the ventral edge (arrows, Fig. 44F, instars IV and V only).

Rivers, also occasionally on lake-shores; associated with large stones. Widespread and common in Britain, rarer in Ireland. Overwinters at instar V.

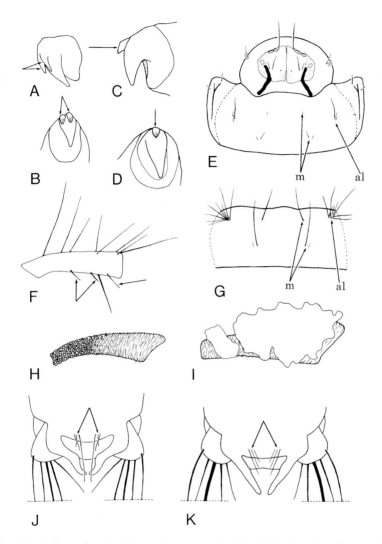

Fig. 44. **A–D:** anal proleg claw and accessory hook(s): A, B, *Ceraclea albimacula*; C, D, *C. senilis*. **E:** mesothorax and metathorax, dorsal view, of *C. albimacula*. **F:** tibia of 2nd leg, anterior view, of *C. annulicornis*. **G:** metadorsum of *C. annulicornis*. **H, I:** case: H, *C. albimacula*, instar III; I, *C. fulva*. **J, K:** 9th abdominal segment, dorsal view: J, *C. nigronervosa,* instar II; K, *C. dissimilis,* instar II.

23(17) Mesoventer with setae. Case composed principally of translucent, flexible secreted material; sand grains not incorporated—   **24**

—   Mesoventer without setae. Case composed, at least in part, of sand grains—   **25**

24   Mesoventer with 2 setae on each side—   **Ceraclea fulva** (Rambur)
                                                                        Instar II

       Large ponds and lakes; in sponges. Widespread; common except in south-east England.

—   Mesoventer with 1 seta on each side—   **Ceraclea senilis** (Burmeister)
                                                                        Instar II

       Still or slow-flowing water; in sponges. Ireland, midland and southern England, Dumfries & Galloway; local.

25(23) Metaventer with 2 setae on each side—   **26**

—   Metaventer with 1 seta on each side—   **27**

26 9th abdominal dorsum with 1 seta in each group which is much thicker and longer than the others (arrows, Fig. 44J, p. 113). Found from June to early August— **Ceraclea nigronervosa** (Retzius)
Instar II

Streams, rivers and lakes; stony substratum. Widespread and common. Overwinters as fully grown larva in pupal case.

— 9th abdominal dorsum with all setae in each group more or less alike (arrows, Fig. 44K). Found from August to April—
Ceraclea dissimilis (Stephens)
Instar II

Rivers, large streams and stony lake-shores; on and under big stones, also on submerged tree roots but only in slow-flowing water. Widespread and common.

27(25) Found from August to May— **Ceraclea albimacula** (Rambur)
Instar II

Rivers, large streams and canals. Widespread. Overwinters at instar II (but not necessarily in sponges).

— Found from July to September— **Ceraclea annulicornis** (Stephens)
Instar II

Rivers, also occasionally on lake-shores; associated with large stones. Widespread and common in Britain, rarer in Ireland. Overwinters at instar V.

28(9) *EITHER:* anal region surrounded by tooth-edged plates *tp* (Figs 45C,E);
       OR: anal prolegs with two rows of strong posteriorly-directed spines *pp*
       (Figs 45B,D). Case of sand grains, curved but not conspicuously
       tapering (Fig. 45G)—   Genus SETODES, **29**

—   Anal region with neither tooth-edged plates nor rows of strong
       posteriorly-directed spines on the prolegs; (there may be spinules *p* and
       large soft spines *sp* around the anal slit, as in Fig. 45A)—   **30**

29   *Note: Setal counts are not known for instars II and III (headwidth less
       than 0.23 mm).* Anal proleg with two rows of strong posteriorly directed
       spines *pp* (Figs 45B,D). 1st abdominal segment with only 1 or 2 dorso-
       lateral setae *dl* (Fig. 45F) and 1 ventral seta on each side. Metadorsum
       central area with only 4 setae *cs* (Fig. 45F). Metaventer with up to 12
       setae. Sclerites greyish-brown—
                                     Setodes argentipunctellus (McLachlan)

       Lake-shores; stony substratum. Windermere and Coniston Water (Cumbria),
       Mochrum Loch (Dumfries & Galloway), Lower and Middle Lakes (Killarney,
       Ireland); extremely local, being absent from neighbouring lakes; often abundant
       where found. Larvae that key out as *S. argentipunctellus* have been found
       recently in a river in north Devon.

—   Anal region surrounded by tooth-edged plates *tp* (Figs 45C,E). 1st
       abdominal segment with more than 2 dorso-lateral setae and more than
       1 ventral seta on each side. Metadorsum central area with many more
       than 4 setae (about 20). Metaventer with many more than 12 setae (about
       60). Sclerites straw-coloured—   **Setodes punctatus** (Fabricius)

       Fast-flowing regions of large rivers; sandy substratum. Rivers Severn and Wye
       (England). Very rare, with no records for the past 25 years.

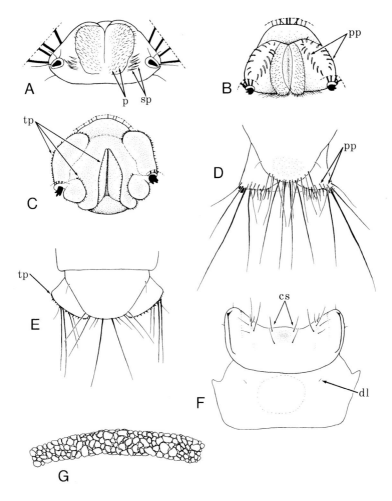

Fig. 45. **A–C:** 9th abdominal segment, posterior view: A, *Mystacides longicornis*; B, *Setodes argentipunctellus*; C, *S. punctatus*. **D, E:** 9th abdominal segment, dorsal view: D, *S. argentipunctellus*; E, *S. punctatus*. **F:** metathorax and 1st abdominal segment, dorsal view, of *S. argentipunctellus*. **G:** case of *S. argentipunctellus*.

30(28) 1st abdominal lateral sclerite (*f* in Fig. 46A) with a posterior projection bearing a conspicuous dark bar *b* (Figs 46B,D); (in larvae with a headwidth of less than 0.20 mm, the bar is rather thin and could be overlooked, Fig. 46C)— **31**

— 1st abdominal lateral sclerite without a dark bar on its posterior projection (Fig. 46E); (sclerite may range from pale straw to grey in colour)— **36**

31 Tibia and tarsus of 3rd leg each with a median constriction *c* (Fig. 34C, p. 91), usually marked by a pale transverse band; (these features are difficult to detect in very small larvae). Dark bar of posterior projection of 1st abdominal lateral sclerite is thin and curved (Figs 46B,C). Head, pronotum and mesonotum with black spots on a yellowish or brownish background. Case straight or slightly curved, composed of sand grains usually with added plant fragments (Figs 46H,I)—

Genus MYSTACIDES, **32**

— Neither tibia nor tarsus of 3rd leg with a median constriction or pale transverse band. Dark bar of posterior projection of 1st abdominal lateral sclerite is broad and straight (Fig. 46D). Head with reddish-orange colouration, pronotum and mesonotum very pale brown with slightly darker spots. Case *EITHER* strongly curved, composed of sand grains coated with secretion (Fig. 46F) *OR* straight, composed of pieces of plant material, usually roots, arranged in a spiral (Fig. 46G)—

Genus ADICELLA *, **35**

* *Adicella* is not known at instar II (headwidth probably less than 0.2 mm) although the separation in this couplet is likely to work at instar II.

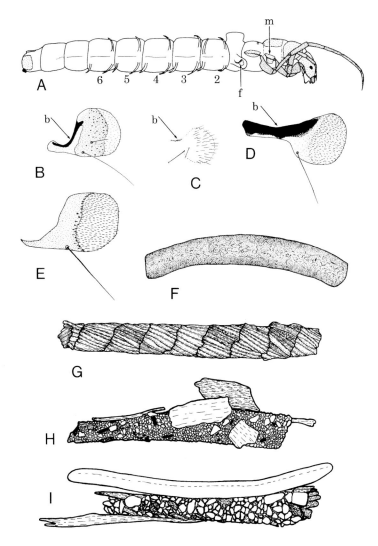

Fig. 46. **A:** larva of *Mystacides longicornis*, lateral view. **B–E:** 1st abdominal lateral sclerite: B, *M. longicornis*; C, *M. longicornis*, instar II; D, *Adicella reducta*; E, *Triaenodes bicolor*. **F–I:** case: F, *A. filicornis*; G, *A. reducta*; H, *M. longicornis*; I, *M. azurea*.

32   Gills present on 6th abdominal segment (Fig. 46A)—
       Mystacides longicornis (L.)
       Instar V (most key out here)

Head pattern like Fig. 47A and NOT like Fig. 47B but beware larvae with overall dark heads where the pattern may be difficult to distinguish. If there is a mismatch between gill and head pattern characters, the user is urged to take the larva through couplet 33 in order to identify it.

Large ponds, lakes, canals and very slowly-flowing large rivers; muddy sand substrata and among vegetation. Widespread and common.

—   Gills absent from 6th abdominal segment—   **33**

33   Posterior half of fronto-clypeal apotome with a distinctively shaped mark (Fig. 47A). Anal proleg claw with 2 obvious accessory hooks (arrows, Figs 47D,E); sometimes a minute hook *m* is present above the claw (Fig. 47E). Ventral part of anterior faces of trochanters and femora of 2nd and 3rd legs with long dagger-like spinules at instar V (headwidth more than 0.50 mm) and numerous spinule combs *sc* and short dagger-like spinules *dp* at earlier instars (Fig. 47F); (a magnification of x200 may be required)—   **34**

—   Posterior half of fronto-clypeal apotome with a pattern of spots, not a distinctively shaped mark (Fig. 47B). Anal proleg claw with 3 obvious accessory hooks (arrows, Fig. 47C), one of which is directly above the claw. Ventral part of anterior faces of trochanters and femora of 2nd and 3rd legs without prominent dagger-like spinules or large spinule combs; (a few small spinule combs may be present)— **Mystacides azurea** (L.)

In most specimens, gills are absent from all abdominal segments, but a few larvae have been found which agree with all of the characters given above except that they possess gills. They seem to be very rare and none has yet been reared to the adult.

Lakes, canals and still or slow-flowing regions of rivers and large streams; stony substratum or tree roots and other vegetation. Widespread and common.

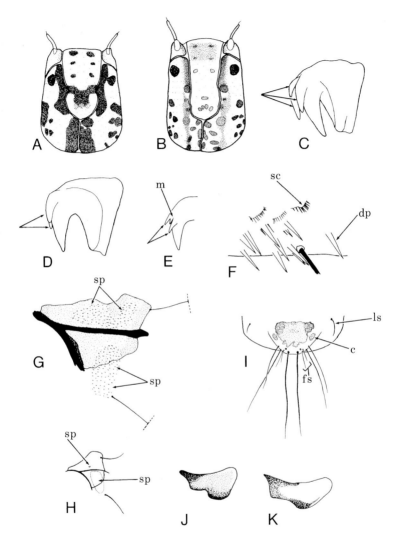

Fig. 47. **A, B:** head capsule: A, *Mystacides longicornis*; B, *M. azurea*. **C–E:** anal proleg claw and accessory hooks: C, *M. azurea*; D, *M. longicornis*; E, *M. nigra*. **F:** mid-ventral region of femur of 3rd leg, anterior view, of *M. longicornis*, instar IV. **G, H:** mesopleurite of *M. longicornis*: G, instar V; H, instar II. **I:** 9th abdominal dorsum of *M. longicornis*. **J, K:** protrochantin: J, *M. longicornis*; K, *M. nigra*.

34   Mesopleurite (*m*, Fig. 46A, p. 119) with a patch *sp* of spinule combs to each side of the central bar (Fig. 47G, p. 121; these spinule combs resemble those shown (enlarged) as *sc* in Fig. 47F); at instars II and III (headwidth less than 0.35 mm) dorsal patch may be represented by only 1 or 2 short spinule combs (as in Fig. 47H); (a magnification of at least x200 should be used)—   **Mystacides longicornis** (L.)

Femur of 3rd leg with large dagger-like spinules on ventral part of anterior face at instar V, dagger-like spinules and spinule combs at earlier instars. Except in dark larvae (characterised by grey-brown to black parietals), 9th abdominal segment at instar V with lateral colour patches *c* on the dorsal sclerite (Fig. 47I) and posterior-lateral setae *ls* which are dark and similar in colour to the fine dorsal sclerite setae *fs* (Fig. 47I); at instars IV and V, protrochantin central area grey-brown (Fig. 47J) and darker than central area of 1st leg coxa.

Large ponds, lakes, canals and very slowly-flowing large rivers; muddy sand substrata and among vegetation. Widespread and common.

—   Mesopleurite with a patch of spinule combs only to the ventral side of the central bar—   **Mystacides nigra** (L.)

Femur of 3rd leg with dagger-like spinules and spinule combs on ventral part of interior face at instar V (as in Fig. 47F), but only spinule combs at other instars. 9th abdominal segment without lateral colour patches *c* on the dorsal sclerite and with posterior-lateral setae *ls* which are paler than the fine dorsal sclerite setae *fs* (see Fig. 47I). Except in dark larvae (characterised by grey-brown to black parietals), protrochantin central area straw-coloured (Fig. 47K) and similar in colour to central area of 1st leg coxa.

Lakes, canals and still or slow-flowing regions of rivers and large streams; stony substratum or tree roots and other vegetation. Throughout England and Wales; also in central Scotland. Usually found in small numbers with one or both of the other *Mystacides* species.

35(31) *Note: Separation has not been tested at instars II and III (headwidth less than 0.30 mm) but the case characters are likely to work for identification.* Case straight, composed of pieces of plant material, usually roots, arranged in a spiral (Fig. 46G, p. 119). 9th abdominal dorsum with 12 setae (Fig. 48A, p. 125). Excluding anterior-lateral setal groups *al*, mesodorsum with up to 10 setae (usually 8) and metadorsum with only 4 setae (Fig. 48C, p. 125)— **Adicella reducta** (McLachlan)

Head pale with reddish–orange bands and spots (Fig. 48D) at instar V (ventral apotome quadrangular, Fig. 48E), uniformly reddish-orange at earlier instars (ventral apotome triangular, Fig. 48F).

Widespread in a large range of flowing waters such as rocky streams, marshes, canals and rivers, especially among roots of marginal vegetation; the only leptocerid found regularly in impoverished large streams.

— Case strongly curved, with a smooth glossy appearance, composed of sand grains coated with secretion (Fig. 46F). 9th abdominal dorsum with 14 setae (Fig. 48B). Excluding anterior-lateral setal groups, mesodorsum with more than 10 setae (16–30 at instar V, ventral apotome quadrangular as in Fig. 48E) and metadorsum with more than 4 setae (11–13 at instar V)— **Adicella filicornis** (Pictet)

Head uniformly reddish-orange at all known instars.

Very small, shallow springs. Widespread but extremely local. Records of larvae in the past 30 years are from sites in Devon, Gwynedd, Wrexham, South Lanarkshire; much older records of adults are from Hampshire and Powys.

36(30) *Note:* Erotesis baltica *is not known at instars II and III. It may swim at* *instar II, as this is common in the family at that instar. Use this couplet* *with caution for larvae with a headwidth less than 0.25mm.*
3rd leg with two long setal fringes (Figs 48G,H); (fringes are sparse at instar II, Fig. 48I); larva readily swims. Case straight, composed of pieces of plant material, usually roots or filamentous leaves, arranged in a spiral (Fig. 49A, p. 127) —   **37**

—   3rd leg without long setal fringes (Fig. 48J); larva does not swim. Case distinctly curved when small but almost straight when full-sized; composed of pieces of plant material, e.g. roots, arranged in two opposing spirals, one dextral and the other sinistral, which meet in a zigzag line along the middle of the dorsal and ventral faces (Figs 49B,C) —   **Erotesis baltica** McLachlan

Head with a distinctive pattern (most obvious at instar V, Fig. 49D); subocular ecdysial line, present only at instar V, has a dorsal branch (arrow, Fig. 49D).

Dykes and fens; among roots. Rare; English Lake District, Cambridgeshire, Norfolk and Isle of Anglesey. Old records of adults from valleys of Rivers Test and Itchen (Hampshire).

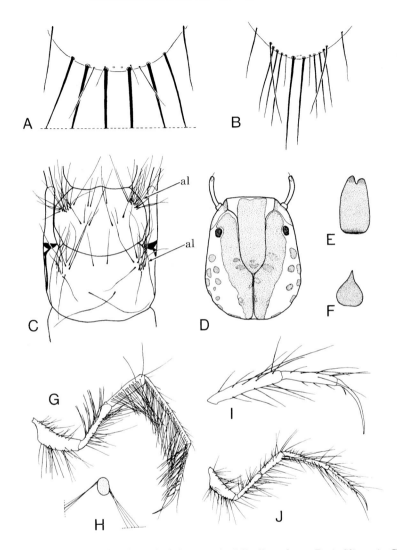

Fig. 48. **A, B:** part of 9th abdominal dorsum: A. *Adicella reducta*; B, *A. filicornis*. **C:** mesothorax and metathorax, dorsal view, of *A. reducta*. **D:** head capsule of *A. reducta*. **E, F:** ventral apotome of *A. reducta*: E, instar V; F, instar IV. **G, H:** 3rd leg of *Triaenodes bicolor*: G, posterior view; H, diagrammatic transverse section of tibia. **I:** tibia and tarsus of 3rd leg, anterior view, of *Ylodes conspersus*, instar II. **J:** 3rd leg, posterior view, of *Erotesis baltica*.

37   Tarsus of 3rd leg with two fringes of long setae, one *a* on anterior face, one *p* on posterior face (Fig. 49E); (anterior fringe is represented by only 1 or 2 long setae at instar II)—   **Triaenodes bicolor** (Curtis)

At instar V (ventral apotome quadrangular, Fig. 50A, p. 129), ventral apotome is as pale or paler than adjoining parts of the genae (Fig. 50A); dorsal head pattern resembles Fig. 50D; 9th abdominal dorsum is dark grey-brown. At earlier instars (ventral apotome triangular, Fig. 50B) all sclerites are grey-brown.

Ponds, lakes and very slow-flowing canals and dykes; among vegetation. Widespread and common.

—   Tarsus of 3rd leg with one fringe of long setae *p*, which arises on the posterior face (Fig. 49F)—   Genus YLODES, **38**

At instar V (ventral apotome quadrangular, as in Fig. 50C), ventral apotome is darker than adjoining parts of the genae (Fig. 50C); dorsal head pattern resembles Fig. 50E; 9th abdominal dorsum is straw to pale grey-brown. At earlier instars (ventral apotome triangular, as in Fig. 50B) all sclerites are pale brown. Not found in static fresh water.

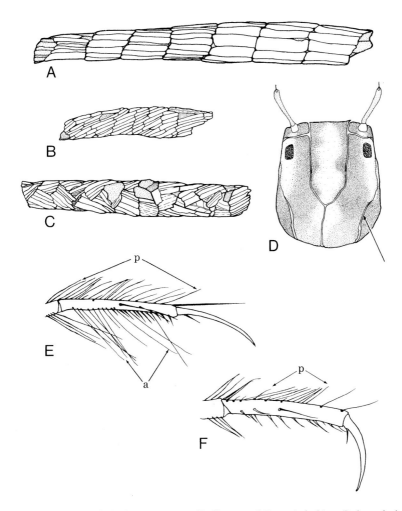

Fig. 49. **A:** case of *Ylodes conspersus*. **B, C:** case of *Erotesis baltica*: B, lateral view, instar IV; C, ventral view, instar V. **D:** head capsule of *E. baltica*. **E, F:** tarsus of 3rd leg, anterior view: E, *Triaenodes bicolor*; F, *Y. conspersus*.

38   Tarsus of 1st leg, in anterior view, with 1–3 short, pale setae on the
      ventral edge (arrows, Fig. 50F)—   **Ylodes conspersus** (Rambur)
                                                              Instars IV and V

      Rivers; among vegetation. Worcestershire and south-east England.

—   Tarsus of 1st leg, in anterior view, without setae on the ventral edge (Fig.
      50G)—   **39**

39   Trochanter of 1st leg, in anterior view, with more than 2 short and pale
      ventral edge setae *ss* and more than 1 dorsal edge seta *ds* (Fig. 50H)—
                                                Ylodes reuteri (McLachlan)
                                  Instar V (and possibly earlier instars)

      Brackish water. Recorded from Orkney, East Riding of Yorkshire, Suffolk,
      Essex, Kent and Co. Wexford (Ireland).

—   Trochanter of 1st leg, in anterior view, with only 2 short and pale ventral
      edge setae *ss* and only 1 dorsal edge seta *ds* (as in Fig. 50I)—   **40**

40   Ventral apotome quadrangular (as in Fig. 50C). Subocular ecdysial line
      sl present (as in Figs 50C,E)—   **Ylodes simulans** (Tjeder)
                                                                   Instar V

      Rivers; among vegetation. Recorded from south-west England, south-west and
      north Wales and River Forth (Perth & Kinross).

—   Ventral apotome triangular (as in Fig. 50B). Subocular ecdysial line
      absent—   **Ylodes consperus** (Rambur)
                                                            Instars II and III
                                                 Ylodes simulans (Tjeder)
                                                             Instars II to IV
                                    and probably **Ylodes reuteri** (McLachlan)
                                                          Instars II, III, ?IV

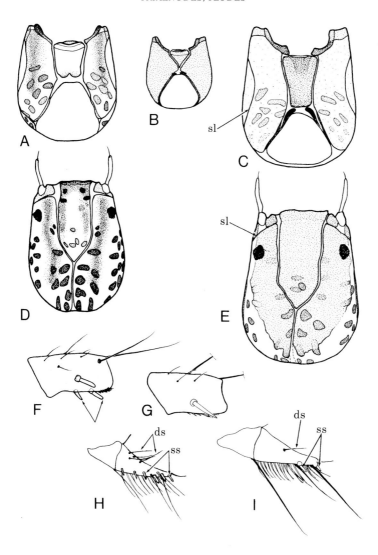

Fig. 50. **A–C:** head capsule, ventral view: A, *Triaenodes bicolor*; B, *T. bicolor*, instar
IV; C, *Ylodes conspersus*. **D, E:** head capsule: D, *T. bicolor*; E, *Y. conspersus*.
F, G: tarsus of 1st leg, anterior view; F, *Y. conspersus*; G, *Y. simulans*. **H, I:**
trochanter of 1st leg, anterior view; H, *Y. reuteri*; I, *Y. conspersus*.

The key to Family Limnephilidae begins on page 131.

KEY TO FAMILY LIMNEPHILIDAE
(TWENTY-ONE GENERA AND FIFTY-EIGHT SPECIES)

The family Limnephilidae is the largest family of Trichoptera in the British Isles, with 58 species in 21 genera (Table 8, p. 132). It is a successful group, the larvae forming a conspicuous element of the fauna in a wide range of habitats. Many species have strategies that enable them to take advantage of waterbodies which only hold water from autumn to spring.

The family has no unique distinguishing feature and the larvae are rather similar to those of the family Lepidostomatidae. The arrangement of the dorsal thoracic sclerites (Fig. 1, p. 15) distinguishes lepidostomatids and most limnephilids from other cased caddis (some limnephilids have modified or ill-defined metadorsal sclerites); all species have a prosternal horn (Fig. 2, p. 16) and antennae which are set well back from the margin of the head capsule. Limnephilids differ from lepidostomatids in the presence of a dorsal protuberance on the first abdominal segment, the position of the antennae relative to the eye (Fig. 13A, p. 39, except in the terrestrial *Enoicyla pusilla*) and the absence of a genal fold (Fig. 13B).

Plant litter derived from overhanging trees and emergent vegetation is the principal food source of most limnephilids; others eat living plants and algae while larvae with toothless mandibles scrape material from surfaces. The main growth period of those species which feed on plant litter falls between autumn and spring, when litter is most plentiful. Two principal strategies are adopted by larvae once they are fully fed. Some species enter a larval diapause and do not metamorphose until late summer or autumn; the larva may remain active or may fix its case ready for pupation and then spend several weeks inside as a larva. This group of species is restricted to permanent waterbodies and the females lay their eggs soon after emergence, under objects in or close to the water. In the other group of species, the larvae metamorphose in spring and the adults enter a diapause, not laying eggs until summer or autumn. These species are able to utilise waterbodies which only hold water between autumn and spring (called 'temporary' waterbodies in the key). The eggs are laid in damp places, such as under logs on the otherwise dry bottom, and do not hatch until the waterbody floods, which may be several weeks later. A few temporary waterbody species rely on early hatching of the larvae which then burrow into the bottom in order to pass through the dry spell.

Table 8. Headwidths of Limnephilidae: ranges (mm) (and n) at instars III to V.

* Not keyed to species at this instar.

[1] Data from D. Harding (pers. comm.). Headwidth range at instar II is 0.38-0.46 mm.

[2] Dagger-like setae are present at the anterior-lateral corner of the pronotum at instar V only.

[3] Data from Garside (1979).

[4] Mainly data from V. Edmonds-Brown (pers. comm.).

Species	Instar III	Instar IV	Instar V
Allogamus auricollis	0.45–0.56 (21)	0.77–0.95 (12)	1.07–1.42 (27)
Anabolia nervosa	—	0.86–1.03 (8)	1.17–1.57 (13)
Apatania auricula	—	0.60 (1)	0.77–0.84 (12)
Apatania muliebris	0.30–0.40 (3)	0.49–0.62 (8)	0.74–0.88 (20)
Apatania wallengreni	—	0.56–0.64 (12)	0.76–0.94 (14)
Chaetopteryx villosa	0.49–0.72 (12)	0.82–1.05 (20)	1.07–1.57 (85)
Drusus annulatus	0.56–0.58 (10)	0.86–0.96 (12)	1.21–1.56 (14)
Ecclisopteryx guttulata	0.56–0.60 (3)	0.88 (2)	1.38–1.44 (3)
Enoicyla pusilla[1]	0.50–0.60	0.64–0.79	0.77–0.98[2]
Glyphotaelius pellucidus	—	1.11–1.37 (6)	1.66–2.02 (15)
Grammotaulius nigropunctatus	—	1.40–1.67 (15)	2.16–2.85 (21)
Grammotaulius nitidus	—	—	—
Halesus digitatus	—	—	1.68–1.91 (24)
Halesus radiatus	—	—	1.58–2.03 (24)
Halesus radiatus/digitatus[3]	0.7–0.9 (62)	1.1–1.5 (115)	1.71–2.21 (132)
Hydatophylax infumatus	0.82 (1)	1.36, 1.42 (2)	1.84–2.24 (5)
Ironoquia dubia	—	—	1.44 (1)
Limnephilus affinis/incisus	—	0.66–0.88 (37)	0.99–1.33 (102)
Limnephilus auricula	—	0.73–0.81 (14)	0.93–1.22 (44)
Limnephilus binotatus	—	1.00–1.17 (11)	1.45–1.85 (32)
Limnephilus bipunctatus	—	1.02–1.17 (15)	1.38–1.71 (24)
Limnephilus borealis	—	1.12 (1)	1.34–1.71 (15)
Limnephilus centralis	—	0.72–0.86 (14)	0.90–1.26 (81)
Limnephilus coenosus	—	0.86–1.06 (18)	1.15–1.42 (42)
Limnephilus decipiens	—	0.90–1.06 (11)	1.20–1.62 (24)
Limnephilus elegans	—	1.24–1.37 (4)	1.72–2.03 (15)
Limnephilus extricatus	—	0.81–0.94 (10)	1.17–1.44 (49)
Limnephilus flavicornis	—	1.06–1.37 (30)	1.43–1.91 (40)
Limnephilus fuscicornis	—	1.12–1.21 (3)	1.59–1.88 (14)
Limnephilus fuscinervis	—	—	1.48–1.58 (12)

(Continued on p. 133)

Species	Instar III	Instar IV	Instar V
Limnephilus griseus	—	0.91–1.07 (50)	1.24–1.46 (32)
Limnephilus hirsutus	—	0.77–0.94 (16)	1.13–1.37 (16)
Limnephilus ignavus	—	0.84–1.02 (39)	1.20–1.46 (25)
Limnephilus lunatus	—	0.83–0.99 (15)	1.26–1.56 (25)
Limnephilus luridus	—	0.96–1.13 (36)	1.33–1.68 (58)
Limnephilus marmoratus	—	1.03–1.25 (29)	1.44–2.01 (79)
Limnephilus nigriceps	—	0.90–0.97 (16)	1.08–1.46 (44)
Limnephilus pati	—	—	—
Limnephilus politus	—	1.06–1.26 (18)	1.44–1.88 (17)
Limnephilus rhombicus	—	1.18–1.46 (15)	1.50–2.11 (39)
Limnephilus sparsus	—	0.94–1.17 (12)	1.24–1.44 (13)
Limnephilus stigma	—	1.04–1.24 (12)	1.43–2.13 (22)
Limnephilus subcentralis	—	0.88–1.05 (8)	1.30–1.46 (15)
Limnephilus tauricus	—	—	—
Limnephilus vittatus	—	0.62–0.81 (11)	0.86–1.08 (25)
Melampophylax mucoreus	0.57–0.85 (8)	0.92–1.27 (16)	1.30–1.62 (25)
Mesophylax aspersus	—	—	1.15, 1.22 (2)
Mesophylax impunctatus	—	0.92 (1)	1.22–1.37 (12)
Micropterna lateralis	*0.81–0.94 (8)	1.12–1.42 (47)	1.55–2.07 (128)
Micropterna sequax[4]	0.68–0.90 (700)	1.02–1.38 (700)	1.44–2.07 (600)
Nemotaulius			
punctatolineatus	—	1.43–1.57 (3)	2.27, 2.75 (2)
Phacopteryx brevipennis	—	0.95–1.06 (10)	1.24–1.48 (11)
Potamophylax cingulatus	—	—	1.62–2.20 (93)
Potamophylax latipennis	—	—	1.77–2.30 (109)
Potamophylax cingulatus/			
latipennis	0.79–0.95 (16)	1.13–1.45 (64)	—
Potamophylax rotundipennis	0.68–0.84 (11)	1.06–1.20 (14)	1.58–1.78 (23)
Rhadicoleptus alpestris	—	0.90–1.08 (13)	1.24–1.47 (7)
Stenophylax permistus	*0.81 (1)	1.37–1.53 (11)	1.67–2.21 (68)
Stenophylax vibex	*0.92–1.03 (21)	1.28–1.58 (27)	1.82–2.20 (49)

Temporary waterbody species are also found abundantly in permanent waterbodies which diminish during summer, exposing margins with suitable egg-laying sites; the adults still emerge in spring. In contrast to these litter-feeding species, spring or summer is the main growth period of the comparatively few species that feed on living plants or algae.

All limnephilids except *Limnephilus pati* are included in the key, though we have had to rely on foreign material or descriptions for two species, *Grammotaulius nitidus* and *Mesophylax aspersus*. Adults of *Limnephilus pati* and *L. tauricus* were recognised as distinct from *L. hirsutus* by O'Connor & Barnard (1981) and the larva of *L. pati* is completely unknown. There are old records of adult *L. pati* from fens and bogs in East Anglia, and recent records from Ireland and the Isle of Man (O'Connor 1980; Ashe *et al.* 1998). At present, most larvae of *Limnephilus affinis* cannot be separated from those of *L. incisus*.

A few points should be noted before proceeding with the key

Primary and additional setae. All first-instar larvae have the same numbers of setae on the sclerites and leg sections. These are called primary setae. Additional (or secondary) setae appear at successive moults in different areas, depending on the species, and therefore are very useful in diagnosis.

Setae on the femora. The primary setal arrangement of the femur (which is retained by many species at the second instar) is shown by Fig. 52F, p. 139. Additional setae may arise along the dorsal or ventral edges (Figs 52G, 67A–F, p. 169) or on the faces (*fs* in Figs 67A,B). Sometimes, the key refers to additional setae on a particular face (anterior or posterior). It is vital to look at the correct face. In the case of detached legs, two features readily distinguish them: the primary face seta lies closer to the ventral edge on the posterior face (Figs 67A,C) than on the anterior face (Figs 67B,D), and the proximal tip of the posterior face is hidden by the trochanter (part of the trochanter is shown in all figures of the femur in posterior view so that they are instantly recognisable).

Additional face setae may be difficult to see against the face of the femur, particularly if they are pale and fine. They are revealed in silhouette when the leg is viewed from above or below against background illumination. This method is also useful when investigating setae on other parts of the body, e.g. the mesonotum.

Setae of the ninth abdominal dorsal sclerite. There are four long and four short primary setae. In many species the four long setae (*I* and *O*) remain very much the longest at all instars, e.g. Fig. 86C, p. 203. In some species additional setae may develop to approach them in size (Figs 63A,D, p. 161, 81F, p. 195). Two conspicuous pits (*p* in Fig. 86C) are present on the sclerite of all species at all instars and should not be included in setal counts.

Problems caused by regeneration. Regeneration following injury to a leg segment or sclerite at an earlier instar can result in an abnormal setal arrangement at later instars. Short or misshapen legs or grossly distorted sclerites are obvious and must be ignored when identifying a larva. In addition, marked left/right asymmetry in setal sizes, particularly if any of the primary setae are involved, should also invite suspicion and suggest the omission of the abnormal part when keying the larva.

Colour patterning. Limnephilids are notable for their prominent muscle attachment spots. In pale larvae these are usually darker than the ground colour but in very dark larvae they may appear paler than the ground. Sometimes these muscle attachment spots have proved to be taxonomically significant, but unless specifically mentioned they are to be ignored and a description of the head as pale or dark refers to the ground colour.

In some waterbodies, limnephilid larvae are particularly prone to becoming covered by encrusting deposits of iron oxide, which can obscure or resemble colour patterning.

Gill position. Position of the gills and number of filaments per gill site is used at several points in the key. Environmental influence on gill numbers is discussed on page 14. A large group of species have only single-filament gills; occasional aberrations occur, so follow the single-filament route through the key if only one gill position has an extra filament.

KEY TO LARVAE

1   Gills absent—   **2**

—   Gills present—   **3**

2   Larva terrestrial. Antenna *a* situated very close to anterior margin of eye
     (Fig. 51A). Anal region with strong setae *ss* aligned parallel to the anal
     slit (Fig. 51B)—   **Enoicyla pusilla** (Burmeister)

     Case conical, curved, made of sand grains with fragments of dead leaves (Fig.
     51C), sometimes entirely of leaf fragments when full-sized.

     Under dead oak leaves around grass tufts, and often in mouse or vole runs.
     Herefordshire, Worcestershire and Birmingham.

—   Larva aquatic. Antenna *a* at least as close to anterior margin of head
     capsule as to eye (as in Fig. 55C, p. 145). Anal region with strong setae
     ss aligned transverse to the anal slit (Fig. 51D)—

                              Instar II of species which have only
                              single-filament gills at instars III to V
                              (not keyed out further)

3(1) All gills consist of single filaments only (Fig. 51E); (look particularly at
      the ventral gills on abdominal segments 2 and 3; included in this group
      is *Apatania* in which two single gill filaments may arise very close
      together at the anterior-dorsal position on abdominal segments 2 and 3,
      Figs 54D,E, p. 143)—   **5**

—   Some gills consist of more than one filament (Fig. 51F)—   **4**

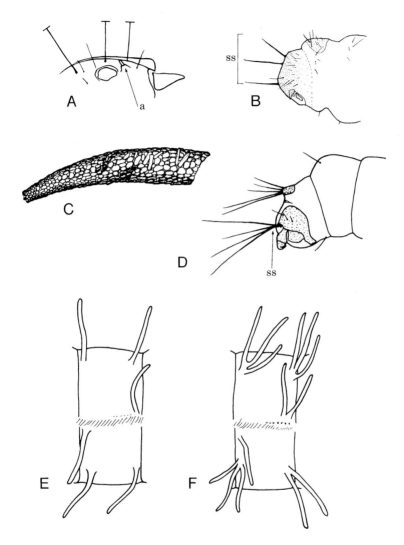

Fig. 51. **A–C:** *Enoicyla pusilla*: A, dorsal part of head, lateral view; B, posterior end of abdomen, lateral view; C, case. **D:** posterior end of abdomen of *Potamophylax* sp., instar II, lateral view. **E, F:** 3rd abdominal segment, lateral view: E, *Potamophylax latipennis*; F, *Anabolia nervosa*.

4   Gills consist of up to 2 filaments only —
      Instar III of species which have some gills with three or
      more filaments at instars IV and V (not keyed out further)

—   Some gills consist of 3 or more filaments —   **33**
                                                              (page 168)

5(3) Larva with ALL of the following features:

      (a) Metadorsum with more than 1 seta on each anterior-median sclerite
          a (Figs 52C, 53A).

      (b) Metadorsum with more than 3 setae on each posterior sclerite *p*
          (Figs 52C, 53A).

      (c) 1st abdominal dorsum with more than 5 setae on each side (Fig.
          52E).

      (d) Femur of 2nd leg with more than 2 setae on the dorsal edge (Figs
          52G and 57G, p. 149) —   **6**

—   Larva with ANY of the following features:

      (a) Metadorsum with 1 seta on each anterior-median sclerite *a* (Fig.
          52A).

      (b) Metadorsum with 3 setae on each posterior sclerite *p* (Figs 52A,B).

      (c) 1st abdominal dorsum with 5 setae on each side, arranged as in Fig.
          52D: 1 lateral *ls*, 1 anterior-median *as*, and 3 posterior *ps* (two of
          which may be very small).

      (d) Femur of 2nd leg with only 2 setae on the dorsal edge (arrows, Fig.
          52F) —   Instar II of species which have some
                                           multi-filament gills at instars III to V;
                     also *Stenophylax permistus* instar II (not keyed out further)

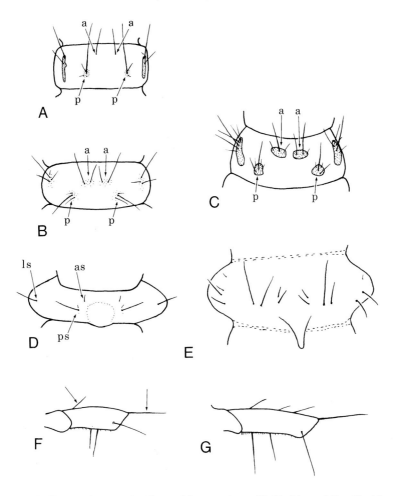

Fig. 52. **A–C:** metadorsum: A, *Limnephilus* sp., instar II; B, *Limnephilus ?luridus*, instar II; C, *Halesus* sp., instar III. **D, E:** 1st abdominal segment, dorsal view: D, *L. ?flavicornis*, instar II; E, *Halesus* sp., instar III. **F, G:** femur of 2nd leg, posterior view: F, *L. ?affinis*, instar II; G, *Chaetopteryx villosa*, instar III.

6   Metadorsum with one or more obvious anterior-median sclerites *a* from which most setae of that area arise (Figs 53A, 55D). Lateral fringe *f* absent from anterior half of 2nd abdominal segment (but may be present on posterior part) (Fig. 53C; setae *lls* are not part of the fringe)—   **10**

—   Metadorsum without obvious anterior-median sclerites though two groups of prominent setae *as* are present (Fig. 53B). Lateral fringe *f* present on anterior half of 2nd abdominal segment (Figs 54D–F)—

Genus APATANIA, 7

Mandibles lack teeth and ridges (as in Figs 56C,E, p. 147).

Case curved, made with small mineral particles (Figs 53D,E).

7   Headwidth 0.56–0.64 mm (instar IV) or 0.75–0.94 mm (instar V)—   **8**

—   Headwidth less than 0.50 mm—   APATANIA spp.

Instar III (not keyed out further)

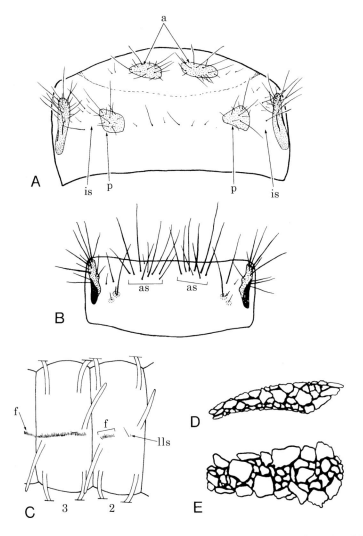

Fig. 53. **A, B:** metadorsum: A, *Halesus* sp.; B, *Apatania wallengreni*. **C:** 2nd and 3rd abdominal segments, lateral view, of *Potamophylax latipennis*. **D, E:** case of *Apatania muliebris*: D, lateral view; E, dorsal view.

8   Setae of anterior edge of pronotum with long, tapering, somewhat flexuous tips (Fig. 54B; those shown are in region R, Fig. 54A). 1st abdominal segment with 14–27 dorsal setae on each side at instar V, 8–10 at instar IV; at instar V the most ventro-lateral seta of the group, vs, is ventral to the base of the posterior-dorsal gill pdg of the segment, if that gill is present (Fig. 54D) —   **Apatania muliebris** McLachlan
Instars IV and V

Head predominantly brown with a slightly paler area in the centre of the posterior half of the fronto-clypeal apotome (Fig. 55A); posterior-lateral muscle attachment spots slightly paler than adjacent area of gena though they have dark outlines.

Small streams and trickles, apparently always near springs; also in a river on the Isle of Man. Stony substratum. Widespread but very local.

—   Setae of anterior edge of pronotum sword- or dagger-shaped, never with long tapering tips (Fig. 54C). 1st abdominal segment with 4–10 dorsal setae on each side at instar V (Figs 54E,F), 4–6 at instar IV; at instar V the most ventro-lateral seta of the group, vs, is dorsal to the base of the posterior-dorsal gill pdg of the segment, if that gill is present (Fig. 54E) —   **9**

9   Anal proleg lateral sclerite with 6–8 setae ps along the posterior edge at instar V (Fig. 54G), 5–7 at instar IV (look at both prolegs). 9th abdominal dorsum with 30–47 setae ds at instar V (Fig. 54G), 21–26 at instar IV. 2nd abdominal segment with 1 anterior-dorsal gill adg on each side (Fig. 54F); 1st abdominal segment without posterior-dorsal gills (Fig. 54F) —   **Apatania wallengreni** McLachlan
Instars iV and V

Head predominantly pale yellow with irregular grey-brown areas and very dark posterior-lateral muscle attachment spots at instar V (Fig. 55C, p. 145), overall darker at instar IV.

Lake-shores; stony substratum. Scotland, English Lake District (Cumbria), Llyn Tegid (Gwynedd) and western Ireland; locally common.

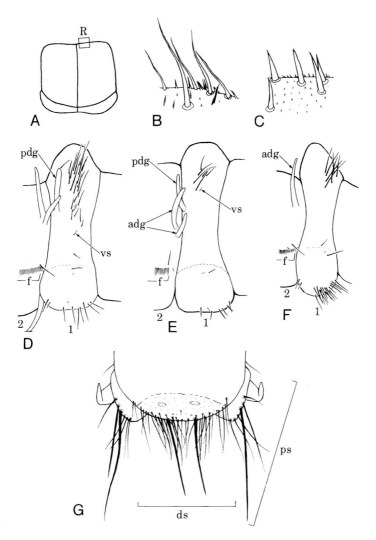

Fig. 54. **A:** outline of pronotum, dorsal view, of *Apatania* sp. **B, C:** anterior edge of pronotum in region *R* of Fig. 54A: B, *Apatania muliebris*; C, *A. wallengreni*. **D–F:** 1st abdominal segment and anterior part of 2nd abdominal segment, lateral view: D, *A. muliebris*; E, *A. auricula*; F, *A. wallengreni*. **G:** 9th abdominal segment, dorsal view, of *A. wallengreni*.

— Anal proleg lateral sclerite with only 5 setae along the posterior edge. 9th abdominal dorsum with 21–26 setae at instar V, about 17 at instar IV. 2nd abdominal segment with 2 anterior-dorsal gills *adg* on each side at instar V (Fig. 54E, p. 143), 1 at instar IV; 1st abdominal segment usually with posterior-dorsal gill *pdg* (Fig. 54E)— **Apatania auricula** (Forsslund) Instars IV and V

Head similar to that of *A. muliebris* but has a paler posterior-lateral region with dark muscle attachment spots (Fig. 55B).

Lake-shores; stony substratum. South-west Ireland only; abundant.

10(6) Metadorsum with one central anterior-median sclerite *a* (Fig. 55D)*. 1st abdominal venter with 2 large median sclerites *m*, each bearing several setae (Fig. 55E)— **Hydatophylax infumatus** (McLachlan)

Femora of 2nd and 3rd legs without additional proximo-dorsal or face setae (as in Fig. 57G, p. 149). 2nd abdominal segment lacks anterior gills. Case resembles Figs 58A,B, p. 151, but is made of dead wood at instar V.

Among woody debris (on which the larvae feed); in flowing water or occasionally on stony lake-shores. Widespread; never abundant.

— Metadorsum with 2 anterior-median sclerites *a* (Fig. 53A)*. 1st abdominal venter without large median sclerites (Fig. 55F)—   **11**

* The central area of the sclerite in *Hydatophylax* is pale and the larvae are often covered in silt; either factor may give the false impression that two sclerites are present.

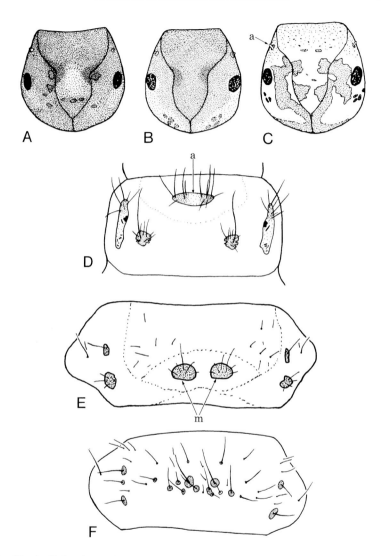

Fig. 55. **A–C:** head capsule: A, *Apatania muliebris*; B, *A. auricula*; C, *A. wallengreni*. **D:** metathorax, dorsal view, of *Hydatophylax infumatus*. **E, F:** 1st abdominal segment, ventral view: E, *H. infumatus*; F, *Allogamus auricollis*.

11   Mandibles with teeth along edges (Fig. 56A) and with ridges in central
     concavity; (teeth may be seen best from in front, Fig. 56B)—   **14**

—   Mandibles without teeth along edges (Figs 56C,E), except that 1 tooth *t*
     may be present on dorsal edge (Fig. 56D); central concavity without
     ridges—   **12**

12   Femora with additional setae *fs* on the faces (as in Figs 62D–L, p. 159)*.
     1st abdominal lateral protuberance without a posterior sclerite but with
     anterior setae *aps* at a median position (Figs 56F,G); (at instar V
     the setae form a conspicuous band but at instar III only 1 or 2 are
     present)—   **13**

     Case curved, made of mineral particles at all instars (Fig. 56H).

—   All femora without additional setae on the faces (as in Figs 57E–G, p.
     149)*. 1st abdominal lateral protuberance with a posterior sclerite *s* but
     without anterior setae at a median position (as in Figs 60C,D, p. 155)—
                                        Melampophylax mucoreus (Hagen)

     * See page 134.

     All sclerites dark brown or black. Case curved, made mainly with mineral
     particles at instar V but plant fragments occasionally predominate at instar III.

     Streams and rivers, one lake-shore (Malham Tarn, North Yorkshire); stony
     substratum; commonest in alkaline waters. England, Wales and southern
     Scotland; may be locally abundant.

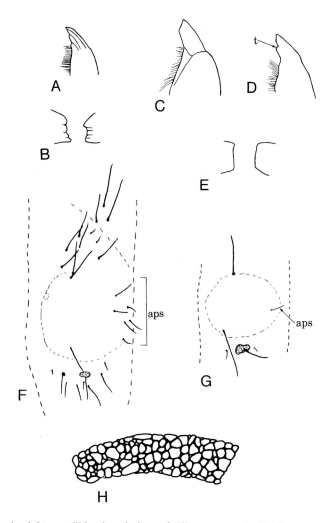

Fig. 56. **A:** right mandible, dorsal view, of *Allogamus auricollis*. **B:** worn mandibles of *Potamophylax cingulatus* viewed from in front. **C, D:** right mandible, dorsal view: C, *Drusus annulatus*; D, *Melampophylax mucoreus*. **E:** worn mandibles of *M. mucoreus* viewed from in front. **F, G:** 1st abdominal segment, lateral region, of *D. annulatus*: F, instar V; G, instar III. **H:** case of *D. annulatus*.

13 Parietal with a group of pale setae *ps* between the eye and the fronto-clypeal apotome (Fig. 57A); (these setae are very obvious at instar V but are not conspicuous at instar III; those close to the fronto-clypeal apotome are easiest to see, Fig. 57B)— **Ecclisopteryx guttulata** (Pictet)*

Head yellow-brown at instars IV and V, darker at instar III. Head and pronotum without conspicuous surface sculpturing.

Large streams and rivers; stony substratum. Locally common in northern and western Britain; also recorded from eastern Ireland.

* Pitsch (1993) claims that descriptions of British larvae of *E. guttulata* and the male figured by Macan (1973) are *E. dalecarlica* Kolenati, 1848, a species that has never been regarded as British. The status of the two species requires investigation.

— Parietal without a group of pale setae between the eye and the fronto-clypeal apotome (Fig. 57C)— **Drusus annulatus** Stephens

Head dark brown at all instars. Head and pronotum with conspicuous granular surface sculpturing (Fig. 57D).

Usually in streams, less common in rivers, rare on lake-shores; stony substratum and among weeds. Widespread and common.

14(11) At least one femur of the 2nd and 3rd legs with 1 or more setae *pds proximal* to the large primary proximal seta *pps* on the dorsal edge (Figs 57E,F)— Genus HALESUS, **15**
Instars IV, V
and about two-thirds of instar III

Mesopleurite ventral process *vp* without setae (Fig. 57H). Case made with large plant fragments (Figs 58A,B, p. 151); cases constructed solely with mineral material are rare.

— No femur of the 2nd and 3rd legs with any setae *proximal* to the large primary seta *pps* on the dorsal edge (Fig. 57G)— **18**

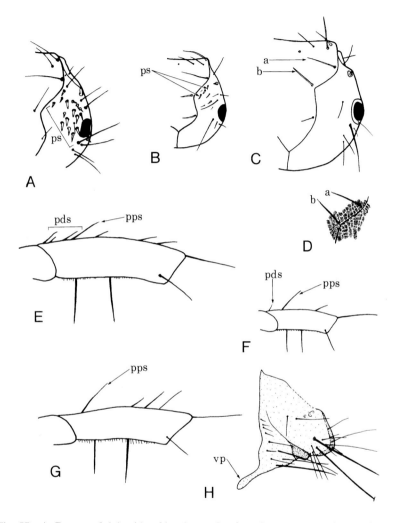

Fig. 57. **A, B:** part of right side of head capsule of *Ecclisopteryx guttulata*: A, instar V; B, instar III. **C:** part of right side of head capsule of *Drusus annulatus*. **D:** surface sculpturing of head of *D. annulatus* in the area of setae *a* and *b*, Fig. 57C. **E–G:** femur of 2nd leg, posterior view: E, *Halesus* sp., instar V; F, *Halesus* sp., instar III; G, *Chaetopteryx villosa*. **H:** mesopleurite of *Halesus* sp.

Important notes: *The dark and pale colour patterns of* Halesus *described below in couplets 15 to 17 are due to pigmentation that is close to the surface of the sclerites; colour differences due to thickness of sclerites or underlying elements seen through them should be discounted. These surface patterns are difficult to distinguish in long-preserved larvae if the sclerites have darkened to orange and the surface pigmentation has faded.*

Both species of Halesus *are very common and frequently occur together.*

15   Anterior lateral region of head with a pale patch *p* that is clear of dark brown surface pigmentation (Fig. 58C); (patch may be as small as in Fig. 58F) AND/OR lateral line fringe present at posterior end of 2nd abdominal segment (arrow Fig. 58H) *; (the fringe may be represented by only a few elements)—   **Halesus radiatus** (Curtis)
                                              Instar V (most key out here)
                                       and some at Instars III and IV

Pale patch *p* as pale as or paler than the posterior-lateral area of the gena *g* (Fig. 58C). Case tube usually rough in outline (Figs 58A,B), not made from smoothly-butted leaf fragments; long sticks may be included.

Streams, rivers and lake-shores. Widespread and common.

* The proportion of larvae that key out here varies between populations. Panzenbock & Waringer (1997) recorded 86% of *H. radiatus* with the lateral line feature but it was present in less than half of the British material that we have examined.

—   Anterior lateral region of head without a pale patch, or with an area that is heavily flecked with dark brown surface pigmentation (Figs 58D,G), or with a very narrow pale band adjacent to the thickened anterior margin of the head (Fig. 58E). Lateral line fringe absent from posterior end of 2nd abdominal segment—   **16**

16   Headwidth more than 1.60 mm—   **17**

—   Headwidth less than 1.60 mm—   **Halesus** species
                                              Instar III and some Instar IV

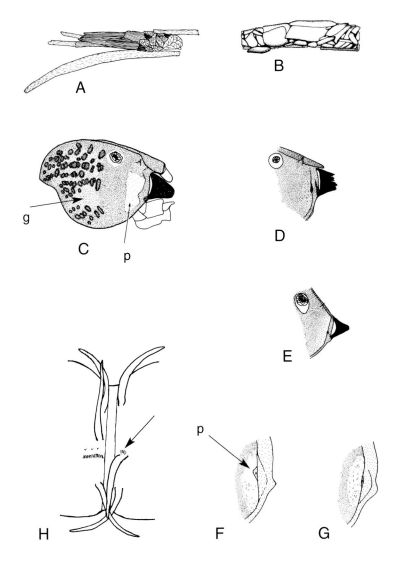

Fig. 58. **A:** case of *Halesus* sp., instar III. **B:** case of *Halesus radiatus*. **C:** head, lateral view, of *H. radiatus*. **D, E:** anterior-lateral part of head capsule: D, *H. digitatus*; E, *H. digitatus,* instar III. **F, G:** pale patch of anterior-lateral part of head capsule: F, *H. radiatus*; G, *Halesus* species undetermined. **H:** anterior part of 3rd abdominal segment and posterior part of 2nd abdominal segment, lateral view, of *H. radiatus*.

17   *Note: Data from Garside (1979) and Panzenbock & Waringer (1997) fit our own observations, suggesting that over 90% of the larvae keying out at this couplet will be* H. digitatus. *The following characters are provided to give extra confidence to a diagnosis. Larvae which do not fit well should be regarded as unidentifiable to species.*

Central region of pronotum (*R* in Fig. 59A) with an unbroken area of brown surface pigmentation which runs down each side of the mid-line and links the coloured patch associated with the transverse groove to the coloured patch associated with the posterior margin (Fig. 59B); (almost invariably the pronotum will need cleaning to remove adherent debris in order to check this character)*— **Halesus digitatus** (Schrank)
Instar V

Posterior region of fronto-clypeal apotome with *both* sides generally converging towards the mid-line for some distance in front of the posterior setae *ps*, so that its widest part *w* lies at the level of setae *ps* (Fig. 59F).

A smooth case made with carefully-butted leaf-fragments (as in Fig. 62C, p. 159), to which long sticks may be added, is characteristic of *H. digitatus* but the species is also frequently found in cases identical with those made by *H. radiatus* (Figs 58A,B).

Streams and rivers; commoner than *H. radiatus* in small streams, less frequent than *H. radiatus* in rivers. Widespread and common.

—   Central region of pronotum without an unbroken area of surface pigmentation running down each side of the mid-line; the colour patch associated with the transverse groove and any colour patch associated with the posterior margin are not linked (Fig. 59C)*— **Halesus radiatus** (Curtis)
Instar V (some)

Posterior region of fronto-clypeal apotome with *both* sides generally diverging from the mid-line for some distance in front of the posterior setae *ps*, so that its widest part *w* lies anterior to setae *ps* (Fig. 59E).

See couplet 15 on page 150 for case and habitat.

* Intermediate examples of both species exist, in which pigmentation is present in the form of discontinuous mottling (Fig. 59D); such specimens cannot be identified using this character.

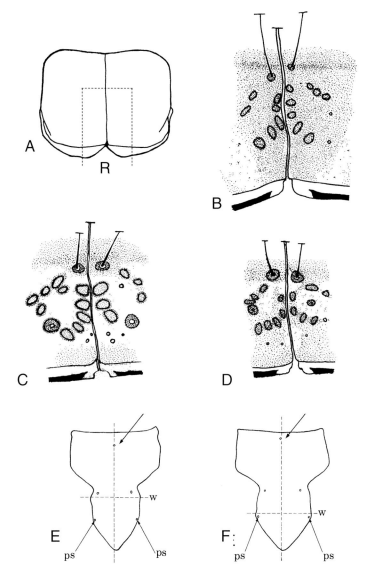

Fig. 59. **A:** pronotum of *Halesus* sp. showing the area that is illustrated in more detail in B–D. **B–D:** posterior-central area of pronotum: B, *H. digitatus*; C, *H. radiatus*; D, *Halesus* species undetermined. **E, F:** fronto-clypeal apotome (vertical line from apex to median pit (arrowed) is the mid-line): E, *H. radiatus*; F, *H. digitatus*.

18(14) 1st abdominal lateral protuberance with anterior setae *aps* at a median position (Figs 60A,B); (at instar V the setae form a conspicuous band but at instar III only 1 or 2 are present)— **Allogamus auricollis** (Pictet)

All sclerites dark brown or black. 9th abdominal dorsal sclerite with 2 central intermediate setae *C* (Fig. 60E); the anterior intermediate setae *A* are shorter than setae *C* (Fig. 60E). Mesopleurite ventral process *vp* with at least 1 seta (as in Fig. 63E, p. 161). Case long and narrow, made entirely with small mineral particles (Fig. 60F) except at instar III when a few plant fragments may be incorporated.

Large streams and rivers; stony substratum. Scotland and northern England; may be locally abundant. Single adults taken in Essex and south Wales but so far no larvae have been found there.

—   1st abdominal lateral protuberance without anterior setae at a median position (Figs 60C,D)—   **19**

19   Posterior region of 1st abdominal lateral protuberance with a large sclerite *s* which lacks setae but has 1–3, usually 2, holes (Figs 60C,D); (sclerite may be very pale, particularly in small larvae, but its smooth shiny surface will distinguish it from the surrounding cuticle). Femora of 2nd and 3rd legs never with additional setae on the faces (as in Fig. 57G, p. 149)*—   **25**

—   Posterior region of 1st abdominal lateral protuberance either without a sclerite (Fig. 61A) or with 1–3 small separate sclerites *s* which lack setae but have a large central hole (Fig. 61B). Femora of 2nd and 3rd legs may have additional setae *fs* on the faces (Figs 62D–L, p. 159)*—   **20**

* See page 134.

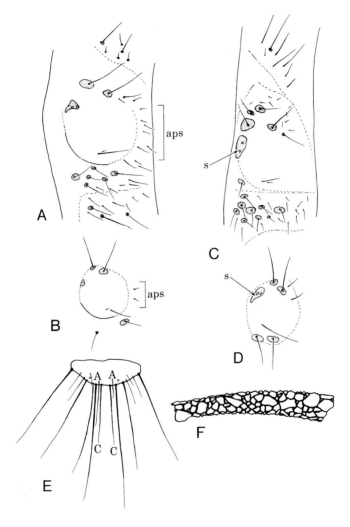

Fig. 60. **A–D:** 1st abdominal segment, lateral region: A, *Allogamus auricollis*, instar
V; B, *A. auricollis*, instar III; C, *Potamophylax cingulatus*, instar V; D,
Potamophylax sp., instar III; **E:** 9th abdominal dorsal sclerite of *A. auricollis*.
F: case of *A. auricollis*.

20   Head with spinules restricted to a small patch *sp* behind the eye (Fig. 61C); (spinules appear as tiny dark points at x50 to x100 magnification but at x400 are seen to be conical outgrowths of the cuticle, *p* in Fig. 61D; the spinules may lie under a deposit of silt, which should be removed)—   Genus STENOPHYLAX, **21**

Stenophylax species are not separable at instar III: headwidth less than 1.20 mm.

Case straight, made with butted leaf fragments (Fig. 62A, p. 159).

—   Head with spinules over most of the dorsal surface of the parietal and often also on the fronto-clypeal apotome (Fig. 61E); (spinules in area *sp* may be slightly more prominent than those elsewhere)—
                                            Genus MICROPTERNA, **24**

Micropterna species are not separable at instar III: headwidth less than 1.00 mm.

Case almost always slightly curved, made with mineral particles and/or butted leaf fragments (Figs 62B,C, p. 159).

21   Additional setae *fs* (Fig. 62D) present on the anterior face of at least three of the four femora of the 2nd and 3rd legs * —
                                    Stenophylax permistus McLachlan
                                            Instars IV (most) and V

Length *l* of femur of 2nd leg[†] (Fig. 62D) at least twice the width of labrum.

[†] NOTE: Both left and right femora should be measured and then averaged, unless one is malformed.

Temporary, slow-flowing ditches and runnels under deciduous trees. Widespread and common.

—   Additional setae absent from the anterior face of at least three of the four femora of the 2nd and 3rd legs * —   **22**

* See page 134.

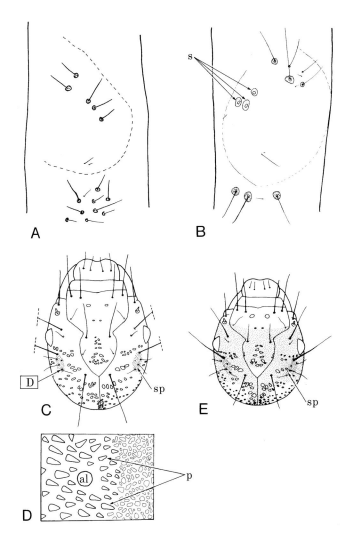

Fig. 61. **A, B:** 1st abdominal segment, lateral region: A, *Micropterna sequax*; B, *Stenophylax permistus*. **C:** head of *S. vibex*. **D:** detail of edge of spinule patch of *S. vibex*, area *sp* arrowed in Fig. 61C (*al* = setal alveolus; *p* = conical outgrowths). **E:** head of *M. sequax*.

22   Headwidth more than 1.60 mm—   **Stenophylax vibex** (Curtis)
                                                              Instar V

Length *l* of femur of 2nd leg† (see Fig. 62D) usually less than twice width of labrum. [† See note to couplet 21 on p. 156 for measurements of *l*].

Temporary, often fast-flowing runnels in deciduous woodland. Throughout Britain, but local.

—   Headwidth less than 1.60 mm—   **23**

23   Length *l* of femur of 2nd leg† (see Fig. 62D) at least 2.03 times width of labrum—   **Stenophylax permistus** McLachlan
                                                              Instar IV (some)

See couplet 21 for habitat.

—   Length of femur of 2nd leg† less than 2.03 times width of labrum—
                                      Stenophylax vibex (Curtis)
                                                              Instar IV

† See note to couplet 21 and see couplet 22 for habitat of *S. vibex*.

24(20) Posterior faces of femora of 2nd and 3rd legs with additional setae *fs* confined to the ventral third, and typically with at least one row of three *fs* (Figs 62E–H)*—   **Micropterna sequax** McLachlan
                                                              Instars IV and V

At instar V, length *l* of femur of 2nd leg (see Fig. 62D and note† to couplet 21) is in the range of headwidth (w) +0.14 mm to w –0.09 mm; at instar IV, *l* is usually in the range of w –0.09 mm to w –0.19 mm. Case curved, usually made with small mineral particles when full-sized (Fig. 62B) but fragments of dead leaves sometimes predominate.

Small, semi-permanent or permanent streams. Widespread and common.

—   Posterior faces of femora of 2nd and 3rd legs with additional setae *fs* not confined to the ventral third, or with only one *fs* or none (Figs 62I–L)*—   **Micropterna lateralis** (Stephens)
      * See p. 134.   Instars IV and V

At instar V, length *l* of femur of 2nd leg (see Fig. 62D and note† to couplet 21) is at least 0.10 mm less than the headwidth; at instar IV, *l* is at least 0.20 mm less. Case usually curved, occasionally almost straight, made with fragments of dead leaves when full-sized (Fig. 62C) though small mineral particles sometimes predominate.

Small, temporary streams and ditches. Widespread and common.

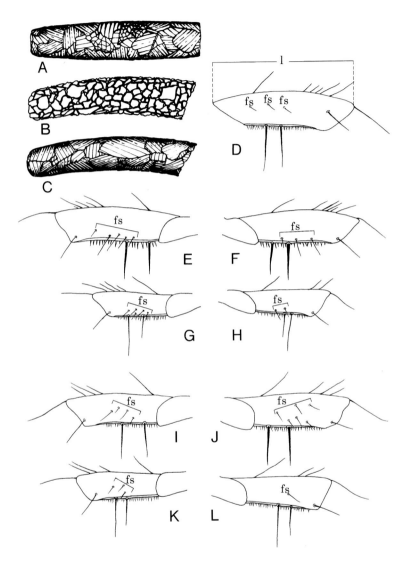

Fig. 62. **A–C:** case: A, *Stenophylax permistus*; B, *Micropterna sequax*; C, *M. lateralis*. **D:** femur of 2nd leg, anterior view, of *S. permistus*. **E–H:** femora of *M. sequax*, posterior views: E, F, 2nd legs; G, H, 3rd legs. **I– L:** femora of *M. lateralis*, posterior views: I, J, 2nd legs; K, L, 3rd legs.

25(19) 9th abdominal dorsal sclerite with both anterior intermediate setae *A*
as long as, or longer than, both of the central intermediate setae *C* (Fig.
63A); (this feature is best seen from the side, Fig. 63B; Fig. 63C should
help to identify the setae) —   **26**
    (*Potamophylax cingulatus* and *P. latipennis*.
    These are not separable at instars III
    and IV: headwidth less than 1.50 mm)

9th abdominal dorsum with at least 2 posterior-lateral setae *pls* on each side at
instars IV and V (Fig. 63A) and sometimes at instar III. Except at instar III, 1st
abdominal dorsum has at least 4 setae *ps* posterior to the protuberance *pr* (Fig.
65B, p. 165). Mesopleurite ventral process *vp* with at least 1 seta (Fig. 63E).
Sclerites of metadorsum and 1st abdominal lateral protuberance brown. Case of
mineral particles when full-sized (Fig. 65A); smaller cases include plant material
and one form resembles the case of *Glyphotaelius pellucidus* shown in Figs
70D–F, p. 175.

—   9th abdominal dorsal sclerite with both anterior intermediate setae *A*
     shorter than the 1 or 2 central intermediate setae *C* (Fig. 63D) —   **27**

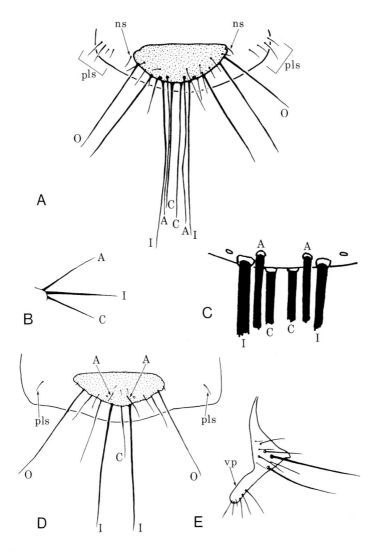

Fig. 63. **A:** 9th abdominal dorsum of *Potamophylax latipennis*. **B, C:** 9th abdominal dorsal sclerite of *P. latipennis*, central region of posterior edge: B, lateral view; C, dorsal view. **D:** 9th abdominal dorsum of *Chaetopteryx villosa*. **E:** mesopleurite, ventral portion, of *P. latipennis*.

26   Pale patch present between the eye and the nearest muscle attachment spots *m* posterior to it (area 2 in Figs 64A–C)*—

Potamophylax cingulatus (Stephens)
Instar V

The coloration of the head varies considerably and a pattern of pale areas (1–4 in Figs 64A,B) may be more or less extensive; occasionally, the band consisting of areas 1–4 (Figs 64A,B) occupies most of the lateral region of the head.

Streams and rivers, also occasionally lake-shores; stony substratum. Widespread and common.

—   No pale patch between the eye and the nearest muscle attachment spots *m* posterior to it (Fig. 64F)*—   **Potamophylax latipennis** (Curtis)
Instar V

Head uniformly dark brown except for area 4 which is often slightly paler (Figs 64D,E).

Streams, rivers and lake-shores; stony substratum. Widespread and common. In river systems, *P. latipennis* and *P. cingulatus* often occur together, *P. cingulatus* predominating in the upper reaches while *P. latipennis* is the commoner species lower down.

*This character has been tested with a large number of specimens from many areas of the British Isles; a few *P. latipennis* with a pale area 2 have been found in Caithness (Highland).

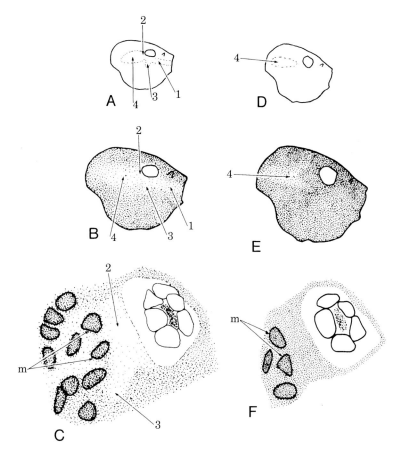

Fig. 64. **A–C:** head capsule of *Potamophylax cingulatus*: A, B, lateral view; C, eye and region immediately posterior to it. **D–F:** head capsule of *P. latipennis*: D, E, lateral view; F, eye and region immediately posterior to it.

27(25) 9th abdominal dorsum with at least 2 posterior-lateral setae *pls* on each side (as in Fig. 63A, p. 161); (do not include any seta *ns* which arises very close to the sclerite)—
Potamophylax rotundipennis (Brauer)
Instars IV (some) and V

Sclerites of metadorsum and 1st abdominal lateral protuberance pale straw in colour. Metadorsum usually with 1 or more setae *is* on the soft cuticle between the posterior and lateral sclerites (as in Fig. 53A, p. 141). 1st abdominal dorsum may have up to 8 setae *ps* posterior to the protuberance *pr* (see Fig. 65B). 9th abdominal dorsal sclerite frequently with 2 central intermediate setae *C* (as in Fig. 60E, p. 155). Case typically made with sand grains, with a distinctive shape when full-sized (Fig. 66F, p. 167).

Streams and small rivers; sandy substratum with stones. Throughout England, but very local; also an old record from South Lanarkshire. Usually found in small numbers.

— 9th abdominal dorsum with only 1 posterior-lateral seta *pls* on each side (Fig. 63D); (ensure that no small, pale seta has been overlooked)— **28**

28 Headwidth more than 1.05 mm—   **29**

— Headwidth less than 1.05 mm—   **30**

29 Sclerites of metadorsum and 1st abdominal lateral protuberance brown in colour—   **Chaetopteryx villosa** (Fabricius)
Instar V

Metadorsum usually without setae on the soft cuticle between the posterior and lateral sclerites (as in Fig. 52C, p. 139). 1st abdominal dorsum rarely with more than 2 setae *ps* posterior to the protuberance *pr* (Fig. 65C). 9th abdominal dorsal sclerite rarely with more than 1 central intermediate seta *C* (Fig. 63D). Case curved, rough in outline, built from mineral particles with some plant fragments.

Streams, also rivers and small upland lakes; stony and weedy substrata. Widespread and common.

— Sclerites of metadorsum and 1st abdominal lateral protuberance pale straw in colour—   **Potamophylax rotundipennis** (Brauer)
Instar IV (some)
See couplet 27 for further information.

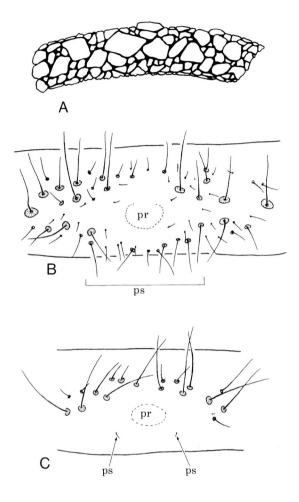

Fig. 65. **A:** case of *Potamophylax latipennis*. **B, C:** 1st abdominal segment, dorsal region: B, *P. latipennis*; C, *Chaetopteryx villosa*.

30(28) Metanotal anterior-median sclerites and 1st abdominal dorsum central area each with an irregular arrangement of setae; total setal count for both metanotal anterior-median sclerites is more than 8 and for the 1st abdominal dorsum central area more than 10 (Figs 66A,B)—

Chaetopteryx villosa (Fabricius)
Instar IV

Case curved, sometimes made entirely with plant fragments but frequently including coarse sand grains.

Larvae at this instar are found in spring and early summer throughout most of the British Isles, but later in the year in upland areas; the life-cycle sometimes extends over two years.

Widespread and common in streams, rivers and small upland lakes.

— Metanotal anterior-median sclerites each with 3 setae (Fig. 66C). 1st abdominal dorsum central area with a regular arrangement of two pairs of setae on each side (arrowed in Fig. 66D); if extra setae are present the total count for both metanotal anterior-median sclerites is 6–8 and for the 1st abdominal dorsum central area 8–10—   **31**

31 Headwidth less than 0.65mm—   **Chaetopteryx villosa** (Fabricius)
Instar III (most)

See couplet 30 for habitat and distribution.

For additional information see notes at end of couplet 32 on p. 168.

— Headwidth more than 0.65mm—   **32**

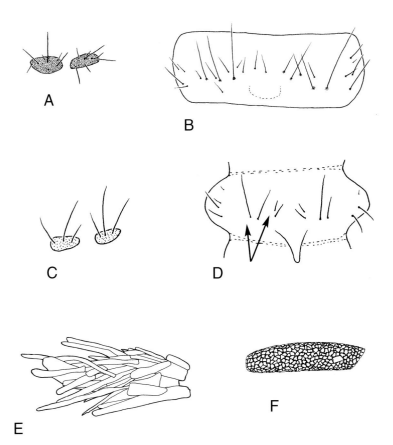

Fig. 66. **A, B:** *Chaetopteryx villosa*, instar IV: A, anterior-median metanotal sclerites; B, 1st abdominal dorsum. **C, D:** *Halesus* species, instar III: C, anterior-median metanotal sclerites; D, 1st abdominal dorsum. **E:** case of *Chaetopteryx villosa*, instar III. **F:** case of *Potamophylax rotundipennis* (instar V).

32   All areas at the bases of setae on the 1st abdominal dorsum (and the posterior sclerite of the 1st abdominal lateral protuberance, and the metanotal anterior-median sclerites) are pale straw in colour. Case curved, made from sand grains with only small and occasional plant fragments incorporated. Larvae at this instar are found in autumn—

Potamophylax rotundipennis (Brauer)
Instar III

See couplet 27 on p. 164 for habitat.

—   All areas at the bases of setae on the 1st abdominal dorsum (and sometimes the posterior sclerite of the 1st abdominal lateral protuberance, and the metanotal anterior-median sclerites) are dark. Cases almost always incorporate large plant fragments. Larvae at this instar are found in winter and spring—   **Halesus** species
Instar III (some)
Chaetopteryx villosa (Fabricius)
Instar III (some)

About one-third of *Halesus* instar III lack the characteristic femoral setae described in couplet 14 (p. 148) and will key out at at this couplet. Larvae with a headwidth greater than 0.75mm will be *Halesus* and it is worth returning to couplet 15 to see if the larva can be definitely identified as *H. radiatus*.

Larvae of headwidth less than 0.75mm cannot be safely separated. However, at this instar, *Halesus* larvae almost always have cases with one or two very long plant fragments incorporated (Fig. 58A, p. 151) whilst use of so few long plant fragments is rare in *Chaetopteryx villosa*, whose case is often as shown by Fig. 66E, p. 167; *Chaetopteryx villosa* cases may include significant amounts of mineral material.

Both genera frequently occur in the same waterbodies but during the spring growth period most *Halesus* larvae will be an instar ahead of *Chaetopteryx*.

33(4) At least one femur of the 2nd and 3rd legs with 1 or more additional setae *fs* on either the anterior or posterior face (Figs 67A,B)*; (if complement of additional 'face' setae is a single seta lying distally on, or very close to, the ventral edge of one femur, follow the second part of this couplet—   **34**

—   No femur of the 2nd and 3rd legs with any additional setae on the face (Figs 67C,D)*—   **60**
* See p. 134.   (page 199)

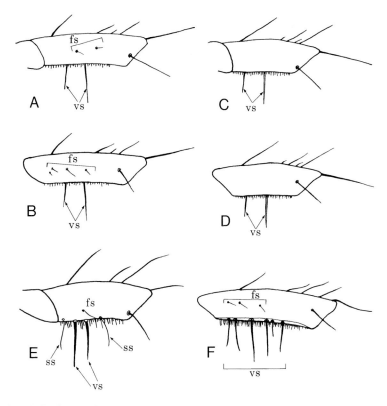

Fig. 67. **A, B:** femur of 2nd leg of *Limnephilus affinis*: A, posterior view; B, anterior view. **C, D:** femur of 2nd leg of *L. sparsus*: C, posterior view; D, anterior view. **E:** femur of 2nd leg, posterior view, of *L. hirsutus*. **F:** femur of 2nd leg, anterior view, of *Mesophylax impunctatus*.

34   Femur of 2nd leg with 2 strong ventral edge setae *vs* (Figs 67A,B,E, p. 169); (1 or more slender setae *ss* may also be present on or near the edge (Fig. 67E)—   **37**

—   Femora of both 2nd legs with 3 or more strong ventral edge setae *vs* (Fig. 67F)—   **35**

35   Gills consist of up to 4 filaments. Metaventer with setae *ms* in addition to the 4 primary setae *ps* (Fig. 68A)—   Genus MESOPHYLAX, **36**

      Head without bands, though fronto-clypeal apotome has a dark mark (Fig. 68B). Case slightly curved, usually made with small mineral particles (as in Fig. 62B, p. 159).

—   Some gills consist of 5 or more filaments (Fig. 68C). Metaventer with only the 4 primary setae—   **Ironoquia dubia** (Stephens)*

      Head with wide brown bands; pronotum and mesonotum with a broad pale stripe along the mid-line (Figs 68D,E). Femur of 1st leg with 3 ventral edge setae *vs* (Fig. 68F). Case strongly curved, made with butted leaf fragments (Fig. 68G).

      Small, shallow streams in deciduous woods. South-east and eastern England; very rare.

      * Ironoquia dubia is not known at early instars. It is possible that instars II and III have gills with 3 filaments but lack characteristic setae on the femora, in which case the larvae may be identified as *Limnephilus centralis* (p. 204).

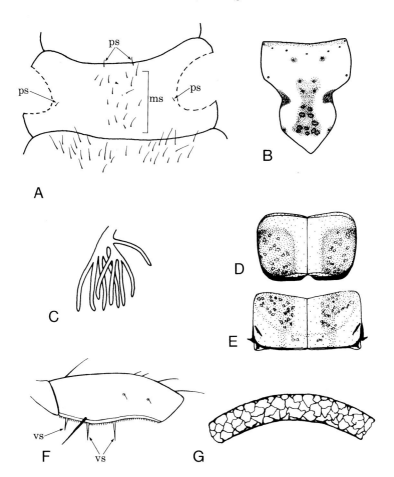

Fig. 68. **A:** metaventer and part of 1st abdominal venter of *Mesophylax impunctatus*. **B:** fronto-clypeal apotome of *M. aspersus*. **C–G:** *Ironoquia dubia*: C, gill; D, pronotum; E, mesonotum; F, femur of 1st leg, posterior view; G, case.

36   Femur of 1st leg with 2 ventral edge setae *vs* (as in Fig. 69B)—
      Mesophylax impunctatus McLachlan

      Exposed lake-shores, under stones on gravel. Scotland, northern England and
      south-west Ireland.

—   Femora of both 1st legs with 3 ventral edge setae *vs* (as in Fig. 68F)—
      Mesophylax aspersus (Rambur)*

      (Based on foreign material and a description by Botosaneanu 1974).

      Streams. Occasional records of adults in southern England; no larvae have been
      found in the British Isles; the species may not breed here (Kimmins 1963).

      * *Mesophylax aspersus* is not known at instar IV. If it lacks the characteristic
      additional ventral edge setae, differences in habitat should distinguish it from *M.
      impunctatus*.

37(34) Femur of 1st leg with ventral edge setae *vs* contrasting in colour, the
       distal seta being dark and the proximal seta pale (Fig. 69A)—   **38**

—   Femur of 1st leg with both ventral edge setae *vs* pale in colour (Fig.
       69B)—   **39**

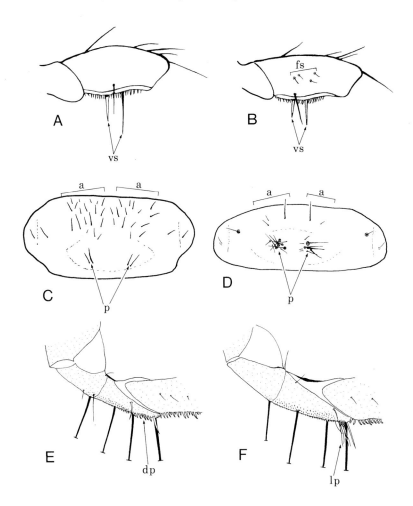

Fig. 69. **A, B:** femur of 1st leg, posterior view: A, *Glyphotaelius pellucidus*; B, *Anabolia nervosa*. **C, D:** 1st abdominal venter: C, *Phacopteryx brevipennis*; D, *G. pellucidus*. **E, F:** trochanter of 2nd leg, anterior view: E, *P. brevipennis*; F, *G. pellucidus*.

38   Femur of 1st leg with additional setae *fs* on anterior and/or posterior faces (as in Fig. 69B, p. 173)*. 1st abdominal venter with more setae in the anterior groups *a* than in the posterior groups *p* (Fig. 69C); no seta in these groups arises from a pigmented area—

Phacopteryx brevipennis (Curtis)
(Some)

Head mainly dark brown, sometimes with posterior tip of fronto-clypeal apotome slightly paler (as in Fig. 88D, p. 207). Distal region of trochanters of 2nd and 3rd legs with a ventral row of stout dagger-like spines *dp* and no, or few, long flexuous spines (Fig. 69E). Case straight, triangular in cross-section, made of disks cut from dead leaves (Figs 70A–C).

Shallow, usually temporary, pools in fens where there is a very slight water-flow; usually under deciduous trees. South-west Scotland, England and Ireland; very local.

—   Femur of 1st leg without additional setae on the faces (Fig. 69A)*. 1st abdominal venter with fewer setae in the anterior groups *a* than in the posterior groups *p* (Fig. 69D); some setae in these groups arise from individual small pigmented areas— **Glyphotaelius pellucidus** (Retzius)

Head brown, usually with small pale patches around edges of fronto-clypeal apotome (Fig. 70G). Distal region of trochanters of 2nd and 3rd legs with a ventral row of long flexuous spines *lp* and no, or few, stout dagger-like spines (Fig. 69F). Case straight, usually with large flat circular pieces of dead leaf attached (Figs 70D–F; note that in small streams, *Potamophylax cingulatus* larvae may build similar cases but they usually incorporate mineral particles whereas larvae of *Glyphotaelius pellucidus* do not), but cylindrical cases of butted or overlapping pieces are common, especially when suitable leaves become scarce.

Still and slow-flowing permanent and temporary waters, usually among fallen leaves. Widespread and common.

* See p. 134.

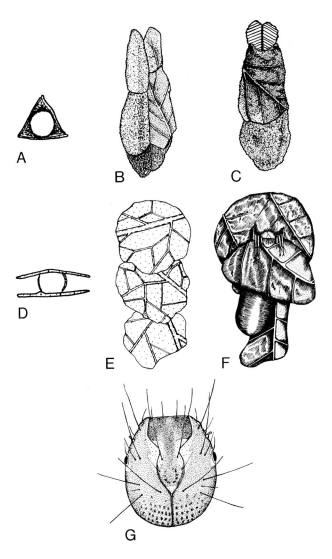

Fig. 70. **A–C:** case of *Phacopteryx brevipennis*: A, transverse section; B, dorsal view; C, ventral view. **D–F:** case of *Glyphotaelius pellucidus*: D, transverse section; E, dorsal view; F, ventral view. **G:** head capsule of *G. pellucidus*.

39(37) Head with a characteristic pattern of dark blotches on a pale background (Fig. 71D)— **Anabolia nervosa** (Curtis)

Femur of 1st leg frequently with additional setae *fs* on the faces (Fig. 69B), (see p. 134). Case straight, either made with plant pieces arranged longitudinally or in a way which produces a chevron pattern in dorsal view (Figs 71A,B) or made with sand grains, often with one or more long sticks attached (Fig. 71C).

Rivers, lakes and ponds; not in temporary waterbodies though larvae may be abundant in marginal pools left by falling water levels. Widespread and common.

— Pattern of head not as above— **40**

40 Head with a characteristic dark 'U'-shaped band on a pale background; fronto-clypeal band *fb* with parallel longitudinal sides (Fig. 71E)— **Nemotaulius punctatolineatus** (Retzius)

Pleural band absent. Case types similar to those of *Glyphotaelius pellucidus* (couplet 38) but green pieces of leaves may be used.

Pools on blanket bog, Caithness (Highland) and ponds near Aviemore (Highland).

— Pattern of head not as above— **41**

41 Anterior third of pronotum uniformly darker than posterior two-thirds (Fig. 71F); (margins and transverse furrow may be even darker, Fig. 71G)— **42**

— Anterior third of pronotum similar in colour to posterior two-thirds (Fig. 71H); (margins and transverse furrow may be darker than rest of sclerite)— **50**
(page 186)

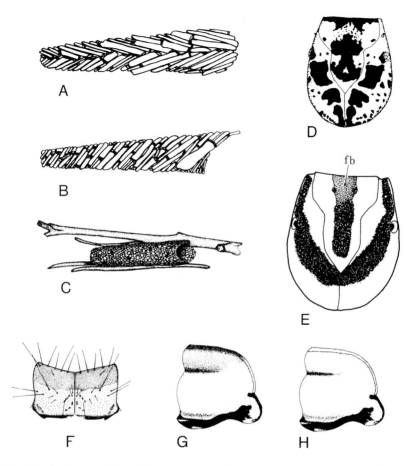

Fig. 71. **A–C:** case of *Anabolia nervosa*: A, chevron type, dorsal view; B, chevron type, lateral view; C, sand grains and sticks type, ventral view. **D:** head capsule of *Anabolia nervosa*. **E:** head capsule of *Nemotaulius punctatolineatus*. **F:** pronotum of *Limnephilus flavicornis*. **G, H:** pronotum, right half, of *L. decipiens*.

42   *EITHER:* proventer (see Fig. 3, p 17) with large lateral sternites that are
      fused with the central prosternite to give a single sclerite which is at least
      twice as wide as it is high (Figs 72A–D, 73A, p. 180),
      OR: case of plant pieces arranged tangentially with their ends protruding
      (Figs 72I–K); (larvae with headwidths more than 1.40 mm have both
      characters)—   **43**

      Case construction often changes during instar V and full-grown larvae may have
      cases incorporating chunks of plant material (as in Fig. 72L), mollusc shells,
      seeds or mineral particles. The prosternites are always distinctive at instar V but
      not always at instar IV (as shown by Figs 72E,F). Head with bands (Fig. 72H).

—   Proventer with small lateral sternites *l* lying a little apart from the central
      prosternite *c* (Fig. 72G), or with indistinct prosternites AND a case of
      plant pieces arranged longitudinally and often overlapping (e.g. Fig.
      72M); occasionally the case is triangular in cross-section (Fig.
      72N)—   **50**
      (page 186)

      NB. Do not continue with the key if the case is missing and the head has distinct
      bands and a width of less than 1.40 mm; the larva belongs either to the group
      covered by the first part of couplet 42 (*Limnephilus flavicornis, L. marmoratus,
      L. politus, L. stigma*) or to one of the following species (which sometimes have
      a dark anterior third to the pronotum): *Limnephilus binotatus, L. decipiens, L.
      nigriceps.*

Fig. 72. **A–G:** prosternites of: A, B, *Limnephilus stigma*, instar V; C, *L. marmoratus*,
      instar V; D, *L. flavicornis*, instar V; E, *L. flavicornis*, instar IV; F, *L. stigma*,
      instar IV; G, *L. incisus*. **H:** head capsule of *L. marmoratus*. **I:** larva and case
      of *L. flavicornis*. **J–N:** cases of: J, *L. stigma*; K, *L. flavicornis* (in transverse
      section); L, *L. rhombicus*; M, *L. binotatus*; N, *L. nigriceps*, illustrating a
      triangular construction.

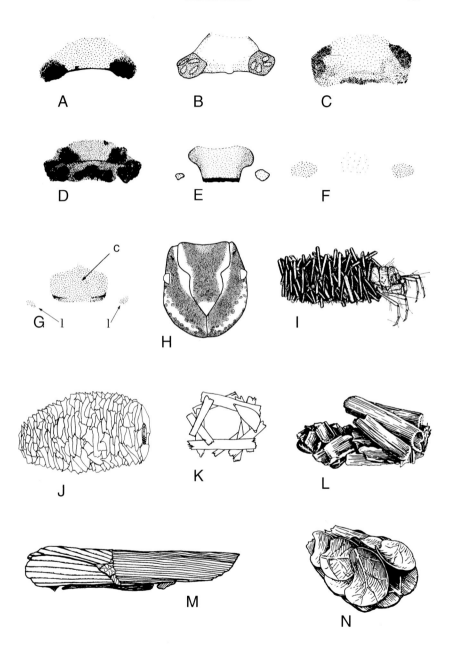

43   Additional setae present on faces of femora of 3rd legs only *; (rarely
     there is also 1 additional seta on femora of 2nd legs at instar V)—
                                         Limnephilus politus McLachlan
                                         Instar V (95%), Instar IV (40%)

Prosternites large and well pigmented at instar V (Fig. 73A); instar IV
prosternites are illustrated in Figs 73B,C.

Lakes and canals. England, Wales and southern Scotland; generally local but
commonest in southern England. Final-instar larvae are found during summer.

—   Additional setae present on faces of femora of the 2nd and 3rd legs *;
     (several additional setae are always present on the faces of the femora of
     the 2nd legs)—   **44**

* See p. 134.

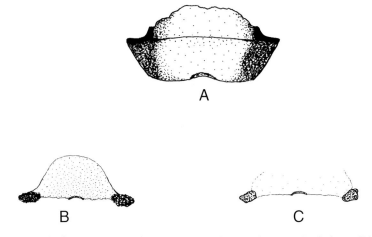

Fig. 73. **A–C:** prosternites of *Limnephilus politus*: A, instar V; B, C: instar IV.

44   Headwidth more than 1.40 mm—   **45**

—   Headwidth less than 1.40mm—   **48**

45   No gills on 8th abdominal segment *—
                                           Limnephilus marmoratus Curtis
                                                    Instar V (some)

Found in a wide variety of still and slow-flowing waters. Widespread and very common. Final-instar larvae can be found from winter to mid-summer.

—   Gills present on 8th abdominal segment *—   **46**

*This character was used to separate *L. flavicornis* and *L. marmoratus* in the first edition of this FBA key but it results in a significant number of larvae of *L. marmoratus* being misidentified as *L. flavicornis*, due to their possession of gills on the 8th abdominal segment; in some stagnant leaf-filled pools, up to one-half of the *L. marmoratus* larvae have been found to have gills on that segment. To date we have seen only one larva of *L. flavicornis* (a bred example) which lacked gills on the 8th abdominal segment at instar V.

46   Proximal section of trochanter of 3rd leg with 2 or more additional setae
     as (Fig. 74A); additional setae may also be present at a similar position
     on 2nd leg. Lateral prosternites merge in colour with central prosternite,
     which usually has patches of very dark pigment (Fig. 74D); a groove (*g*
     in Fig. 74C) runs across the central prosternite (Figs 74D,G)—   **47**

—   Proximal section of trochanters of 2nd and 3rd legs without additional
     setae (Fig. 74B) (or, rarely with one on trochanter of 3rd leg). Lateral
     prosternites contrast strongly in colour with the pale central prosternite;
     there is no groove running across the central prosternite (Figs 74E,F)—
                                                         Limnephilus stigma Curtis
                                                                              Instar V

     Many larvae construct a characteristic massive barrel-shaped case built from
     pieces of grass blades (Fig. 74H).

     Among dense emergent or floating vegetation in marshes which may dry up in
     summer. Widespread; fairly common, except in south-east England.

47   Ratio of headwidth to height of prosternite from posterior margin to the
     groove (i.e. headwidth ÷ *h* in Fig. 74C) is greater than 6.5*—
                                                    Limnephilus flavicornis (Fabricius)
                                                                              Instar V

     Most larvae of *L. flavicornis* have two or more gills on the 8th abdominal
     segment which consist of two filaments.

     Found in a wide variety of still and slow-flowing waters. Widespread; common
     except in the uplands and most of Scotland. Final-instar larvae are found from
     winter to early summer.

—   Ratio of headwidth to height of prosternite from posterior margin to the
     groove is less than 6.5*—   **Limnephilus marmoratus** Curtis
                                                                      Instar V (some)

     Very few larvae of *L. marmoratus* have two gills on the 8th abdominal segment
     which consist of two filaments.

     *The larva must be manipulated so that the prosternite lies flat and *h* should be
     measured at the edge of the prosternite. Use a sufficiently high magnification to
     minimise errors in calculating the ratio. (This character failed for one of 39 *L.
     flavicornis* and three of 65 *L. marmoratus* measured to prepare this couplet).

     See couplet 45 for distribution and habitat.

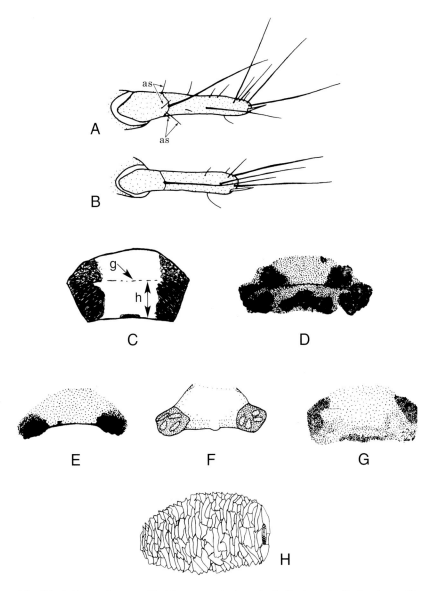

Fig. 74. **A, B:** trochanter of 3rd leg, ventral view: A, *L. flavicornis*; B, *L. stigma*. **C:** outline of prosternites (*L. marmoratus*) showing the groove *g* and height *h* from the posterior margin; **D–G:** prosternites of larvae at instar V: D, *L. flavicornis*; E, F: *L. stigma*; G, *L. marmoratus*; **H:** case of *L. stigma* larva at instar V.

48(44)   Lateral prosternites *l* fused with central prosternite *c* to give a single
sclerite that resembles Fig. 75A—   **Limnephilus marmoratus** Curtis
Instar IV

Gills usually absent from 8th abdominal segment. Case usually made with thin
fragments, as in Fig. 75E.

Found in a wide variety of still and slow-flowing waters. Widespread and very
common. Larvae at this instar can be found from autumn to late spring.

—   Lateral prosternites *l* separated from central prosternite *c*, which may be
very pale (Figs 75B,C)—   **49**

Gills present on 8th abdominal segment.

49   Lateral prosternites *l* much darker than any part of the central prosternite
c (Fig. 75B); central prosternite pale and ill-defined—
Limnephilus stigma Curtis
Instar IV

Characteristic cases made with blades of grass (as in Fig 75D) are less common
than at instar V; cases as illustrated in Fig. 75E are commoner.

Among dense emergent or floating vegetation in marshes which may dry up in
summer. Widespread; fairly common, except in south-east England.

—   Lateral prosternites *l* paler than darkest part (usually the posterior
margin) of central prosternite *c* (Fig 75C); central prosternite well-
defined—   **Limnephilus flavicornis** (Fabricius)
Instar IV

Case usually made with thin fragments, as in Fig. 75E.

Found in a wide variety of still and slow-flowing waters. Widespread; common
except in the uplands and most of Scotland. Larvae at this instar can be found
from autumn to spring.

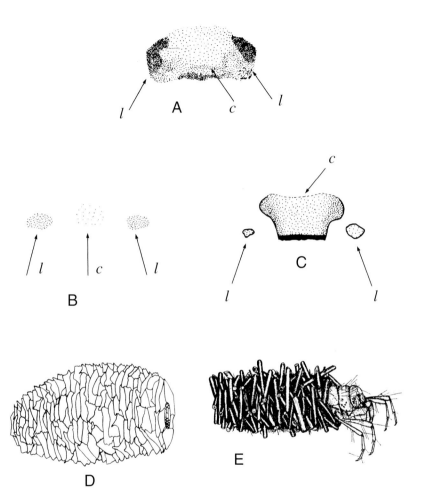

Fig. 75. **A–C:** prosternites: A, *L. marmoratus,* instar V; B, *L. stigma*, instar IV; C, *L. flavicornis*, instar IV. **D:** case of *L. stigma* at instar V. **E:** larva and case of *L. flavicornis*.

50(41,42) Pleural band *plb* long and distinct, joining parietal band *pb* along
the coronal suture (Figs 76A,B)—   **51**

1st abdominal venter with 1–3 setae in each anterior group *a* (as in Fig. 82D, p.
197). Anterior third of pronotum is often much darker than posterior two-thirds.

— Pleural band absent or very indistinct, not joining parietal band along the
coronal suture; (lateral region of head is uniformly coloured or has
brownish patches on a paler background (Fig. 76C)—   **52**

51 Up to 2 (rarely 3) additional setae on each face of femora of 2nd and 3rd
legs; the total count for all eight faces is only 1–5 (one larva seen with 8
setae) *—   **Limnephilus decipiens** (Kolenati)
                                                                (Some)

Case similar to that of *L. nigriceps* (see below).

Lakes, canals and dykes with some vegetation. South-east and midland England
north to Cheshire and Lincolnshire; locally common. Also in central Ireland.

— Up to 7 additional setae on each face of femora of 2nd and 3rd legs; the
total count for all eight faces is 7 or more*—
                                    Limnephilus nigriceps (Zetterstedt)

*See p. 134.

Case straight, made with butted or overlapped pieces of plants, sometimes
triangular in cross-section (Fig. 76D).

Lakes with emergent marginal vegetation. Central Ireland, Scotland and northern
England south to Cheshire and Leicestershire; locally common.

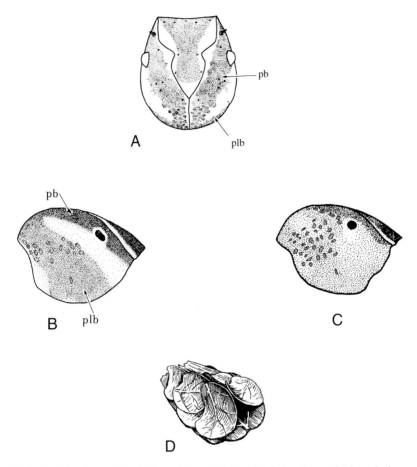

Fig. 76. **A:** head capsule of *Limnephilus decipiens*. **B, C:** head capsule, lateral view: B, *L. nigriceps*; C, *L. affinis*. **D:** triangular case of *L. nigriceps*.

52(50)   Additional setae *fs* on femora of 2nd and 3rd legs confined to proximal region of anterior faces (Fig. 77A); (*fs* absent from posterior faces)*—
Limnephilus fuscicornis (Rambur)

Head predominantly pale (Fig. 77C), sometimes lightly banded. Case curved, made with sand grains and/or plant material (Fig. 77B).

Rivers and streams; among boulders on gravelly-sand substrata. England, Wales and lowland Scotland; local.

—   Additional setae on femora of 2nd and 3rd legs not confined to proximal region of anterior faces*—   **53**

*See p. 134.

53   Case triangular in cross-section, straight (Figs 77D–F). Femur of 1st leg with additional setae *fs* on anterior and/or posterior faces (as in Fig. 77G)—   **Phacopteryx brevipennis** (Curtis)
(Some)

See couplet 38, p. 174.

—   Case circular in cross-section, straight or curved. Femur of 1st leg without additional setae on the faces (as in Fig. 77H)—   **54**

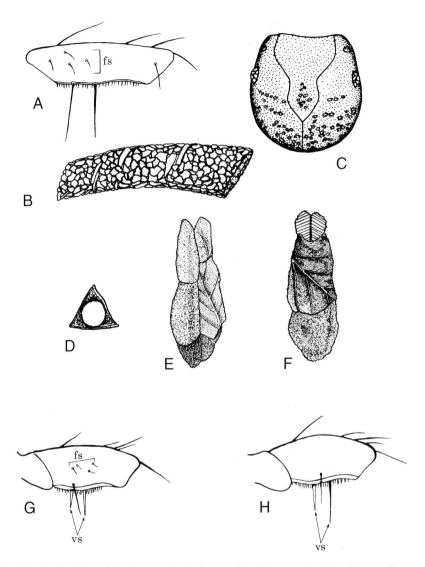

Fig. 77. **A–C:** *Limnephilus fuscicornis*: A, femur of 2nd leg, anterior view; B, case; C, head capsule. **D–F:** case of *Phacopteryx brevipennis*: D, transverse section; E, dorsal view; F, ventral view. **G, H:** femur of 1st leg, posterior view, illustrating presence (G) and absence (H) of additional setae *fs*: G, *Anabolia nervosa*; H, *Glyphotaelius pellucidus*.

54   * Metadorsum (Fig. 78A) with setae *is* on soft cuticle between posterior sclerites *p*; anterior-median sclerites *a* pale and ill-defined. Proximal section of trochanter of 2nd or 3rd leg with 1 or more additional setae *as* (as in Fig. 78C) —   **55**

—   Metadorsum (Fig. 78B) with no setae on soft cuticle between posterior sclerites *p*; anterior-median sclerites *a* dark and clearly defined. Proximal section of trochanters of 2nd and 3rd legs with no additional setae (as in Fig. 78D) —   **56**

      * **Limnephilus tauricus** Schmid will key out here. Information on the larva comes from the exuviae of a single instar-V specimen which was collected by P. D. Hiley among *L. incisus* in a *Phragmites* bed at Woolhampton, Berkshire. The larva had additional setae on the proximal section of the trochanters of the 2nd and 3rd legs and 12 and 16 setae in the anterior-median area *am* on each side of the mesonotum (see Fig. 80C, p. 193). There is no useful data on the metadorsum. Head dark red-brown, without bands (similar to Fig. 88D, p. 207). Case straight, built with overlapped pieces of plant material (similar to Fig. 97F, p. 225). The Woolhampton record is the only recent one for Britain but the species has also been recorded recently from Ireland; there are old records of adults from fens in southern and eastern England.

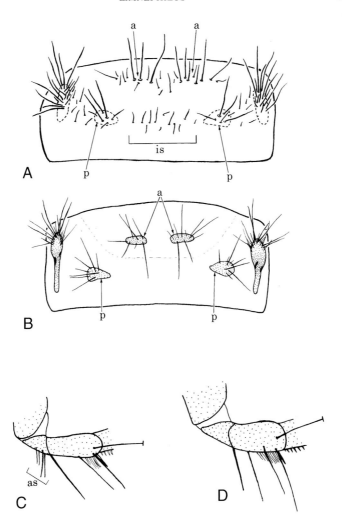

Fig. 78. **A, B:** metadorsum: A, *Limnephilus extricatus*; B, *L. griseus*. **C, D:** trochanter of 3rd leg: C, *L. coenosus*; D, *L. bipunctatus*.

55 Lobe of anal proleg with setae *ls* on soft cuticle by the anal slit (Fig. 80A). Mesonotum with 33–70 setae in each anterior-median area at instar V (headwidth more than 1.05 mm) and 22–37 at instar IV—
Limnephilus hirsutus (Pictet)

Femora of 2nd and 3rd legs with all ventral edge setae *vs* dark in colour (as in Fig. 79A). Head variable in colour but without distinct bands. Case curved, made with sand grains.

Permanent trickles and small streams in open situations, often on bare clay substrata. Not found in acid water. Widespread.

— Lobe of anal proleg with no setae on soft cuticle by the anal slit (Fig. 80B). Mesonotum with 9–31 setae in each anterior-median area *am* at instar V (headwidth more than 1.05 mm, Fig. 80C) and 6–14 at instar IV— **Limnephilus extricatus** McLachlan

Femora of 2nd and 3rd legs with ventral edge setae *vs* usually contrasting in colour (as in Figs. 79B,C). Head variable in colour but without distinct bands. Case curved, usually made with sand grains (Fig. 80D), sometimes with plant fragments, occasionally entirely of plant material.

Silty and well-vegetated regions of small rivers, streams, canals and occasionally lakes. Throughout Britain; common.

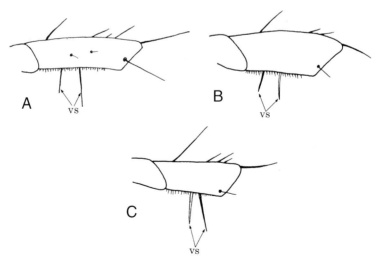

Fig. 79. **A–C:** femora, posterior view: A, 2nd leg of *Limnephilus affinis*; B, 2nd leg of *L. sparsus*; C, 3rd leg of *L. sparsus*.

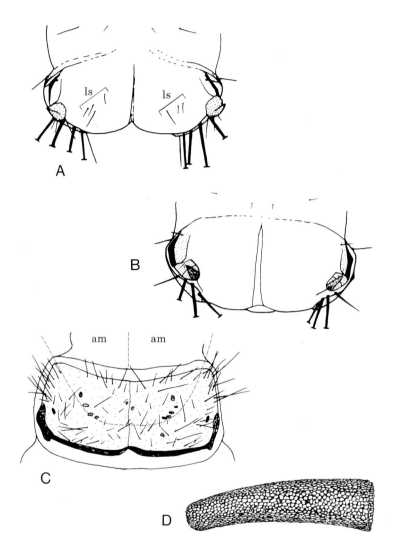

Fig 80.   **A, B:** 9th abdominal segment, posterior view: A, *Limnephilus hirsutus*; B, *L. extricatus*. **C:** mesonotum of *L. extricatus*. **D:** case of *L. extricatus*.

56(54) Case curved (Fig. 81A). Each side of 9th abdominal dorsal sclerite with at least 1 seta between innermost primary seta *I* and outermost primary seta *O* which is more than half as long as seta *O* (Fig. 81F) AND anterior face of femur of 2nd leg with no additional setae (or, very rarely, with 1)*— **Limnephilus griseus** (L.)

Head without bands, though posterior tip of fronto-clypeal apotome is often pale and there may be a pale area on posterior region of each parietal (Fig. 81B). Femora with additional face setae usually confined to posterior face of femur of 3rd leg. 1st abdominal venter with a total of 13 or more setae in the anterior groups *a*, both groups included (as in Fig. 82C, p. 197). Case made with plant material or partly (Fig. 81A) or entirely constructed with sand grains.

Small, often temporary, acidic pools in open situations. Widespread; common in upland areas and lowland *Sphagnum* bogs.

— Case straight (Figs 81C,E) or slightly curved (Fig. 81D). *EITHER:* each side of 9th abdominal dorsal sclerite with all setae between innermost primary seta *I* and outermost primary seta *O* less than half as long as seta *O* (Fig. 81G), *OR:* anterior face of femur of 2nd leg with 1–7 additional setae*— **57**

*See p. 134.

57 Headwidth more than 1.00 mm— **58**

— Headwidth less than 1.00 mm— **59**

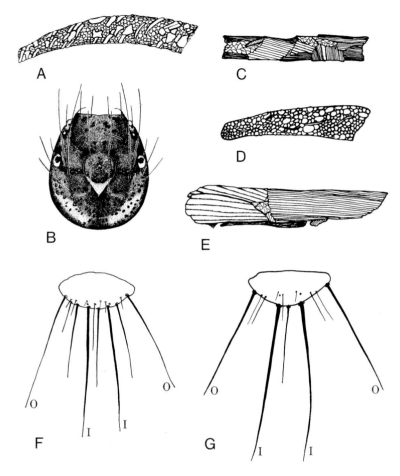

Fig. 81. **A, B:** *Limnephilus griseus*: A, case; B, head capsule. **C–E:** case: C, *L. incisus*; D, *L. affinis*, curved type; E, *L. binotatus*. **F, G:** 9th abdominal dorsal sclerite: F, *L. griseus*; G, *L. binotatus*.

58   Anterior face of femur of 2nd leg with 1–7 additional setae; combined
     count of additional setae on anterior faces of both 2nd legs (Fig. 82A) is
     3 or more. 1st abdominal venter with anterior setal groups *a* large and
     often merged together (Fig. 82C); total number of setae, both groups
     included, is 10–44 (but, exceptionally, as few as 6)—
                                              Limnephilus affinis Curtis
                                              Limnephilus incisus Curtis
                                                                    Instar V

     Head variable in ground colour but parietal bands are usually visible (as in Figs
     88A–C, p. 207). No gills on 8th abdominal segment. Distal section of trochanter
     of 2nd leg, in anterior view, with no dark proximo-dorsal setae between the two
     pale primary setae *ps* (as in Fig. 88G). Cases of both species are made with
     butted and overlapped pieces of plant material, straight (Fig. 81C, p. 195); the
     case of *L. affinis* may incorporate sand grains and small debris (as in Fig. 88H),
     especially if the substratum is devoid of large plant fragments (cases of sand
     grains may show slight curvature, Fig. 81D).

     L. incisus is found in the tussocky margins of pools, lakes and slow–flowing
     ditches which contract or dry out in summer. *L. affinis* is found in similar habitats
     and also in saltmarsh pools. Both species are widespread and common. Both
     have been found together in coastal drainage ditches, freshwater marshes by the
     coast and industrial lagoons with high ionic content; in those situations most *L.
     incisus* are found in the heavily vegetated margins while *L. affinis* is found in
     more open situations.

—   Anterior face of femur of 2nd leg with 0–1 additional setae; combined
     count of additional setae on anterior faces of both 2nd legs is 0–1. 1st
     abdominal venter with anterior setal groups *a* small and distinct (Fig.
     82D); total number of setae, both groups included, is 2–8 (but
     exceptionally up to 14)—   **Limnephilus binotatus** Curtis
                                                           Instars IV and V

     Head brown, with pale areas around edges of fronto-clypeal apotome which may
     be extensive (Fig. 82E), or with a distinct fronto-clypeal band (*fb*) and parietal
     bands. Gills may be present on 8th abdominal segment. Distal section of
     trochanter of each 2nd leg, in anterior view, with one or more dark proximo-
     dorsal setae *as* between the two pale primary setae *ps* (as in Fig. 88E, p. 207) at
     instar V and sometimes at instar IV. Case straight, made with butted and
     overlapped plant material (Fig. 81E, p. 195).

     Among emergent vegetation in fens and lake margins in regions which lack
     standing water in summer. Widespread but local.

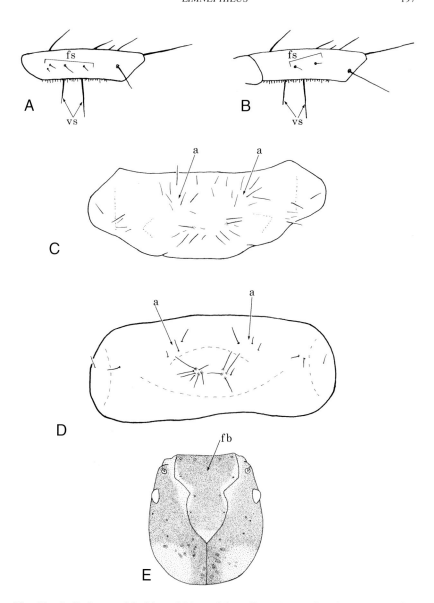

Fig. 82. **A, B:** femur of 2nd leg of *Limnephilus affinis*: A, anterior view; B, posterior view. **C, D:** 1st abdominal segment, ventral view: C, *L. affinis*; D, *L. binotatus*. **E:** head capsule of *L. binotatus*.

59(57) 1st abdominal venter with 5 or more setae in anterior setal groups *a*,
both groups included (as in Fig. 83). Anterior face of femur of 2nd leg
with 0–3 additional setae; (the setae are small and pale) * —
Limnephilus affinis Curtis
Limnephilus incisus Curtis
Instar IV

See notes following the first part of couplet 58 on p. 196.

— 1st abdominal venter with 2–4 setae in anterior setal groups, both groups
included. Anterior face of femur of 2nd leg with no additional setae * —
Limnephilus binotatus Curtis
Instar IV (a few)

*See p. 134.

See notes following the second part of couplet 58 on p. 196.

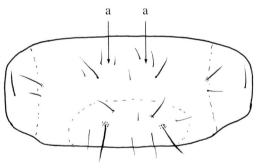

Fig. 83. 1st abdominal segment, ventral view, of *Limnephilus affinis*, instar IV.

60(33) Proximal section of trochanter of 2nd or 3rd leg with 1 or more additional setae *as* (Fig. 84A)— **Limnephilus coenosus** Curtis

Head dark brown, without pale areas. Case curved or straight, made with small pieces of plant material (Fig. 84C).

Small, usually permanent, shallow pools on heather moors and raised bogs. Scotland, Wales and England south to Staffordshire; also Somerset and western Ireland. Common in upland areas.

— Proximal section of trochanters of 2nd and 3rd legs with no additional setae (Fig. 84B)— **61**

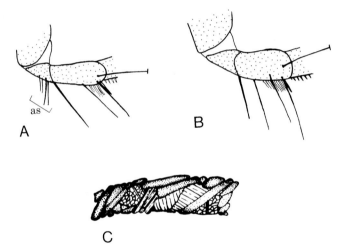

Fig. 84. **A, B:** trochanter of 3rd leg, posterior view: A, *Limnephilus coenosus*; B, *L. bipunctatus*. **C:** case of *L. coenosus*.

61   Case curved (Fig. 85C, and Figs 86E, p. 203, 87B,D, p. 205). Femora of
     2nd and/or 3rd legs with ventral edge setae *vs* contrasting in colour (Figs
     85A,B)—   **62**

—   Case straight (Figs 88H, p. 207, 93F, p. 217, 96H, p. 223, 97F, p. 225).
     Femora of 2nd and 3rd legs with all ventral edge setae *vs* dark in colour
     (Figs 97A,B, p. 225; except in the very rare species *Grammotaulius*
     nitidus, Figs 97C,D)—   **67**

62   Metadorsum with a row of setae *is* on soft cuticle between posterior
     sclerites *p* (as in Fig. 85D; there may be as few as 3 setae in the row)—
                                                       Limnephilus sparsus Curtis

     Head red-brown. Case either made with small plant pieces arranged tangentially
     (Fig. 85C) or made with sand grains.

     Temporary pools, sometimes as small as hoof-prints in marshy ground, usually
     with overhanging grass or rushes. Widespread and common.

—   Metadorsum with no row of setae on soft cuticle between posterior
     sclerites (as in Fig. 85E)—   **63**

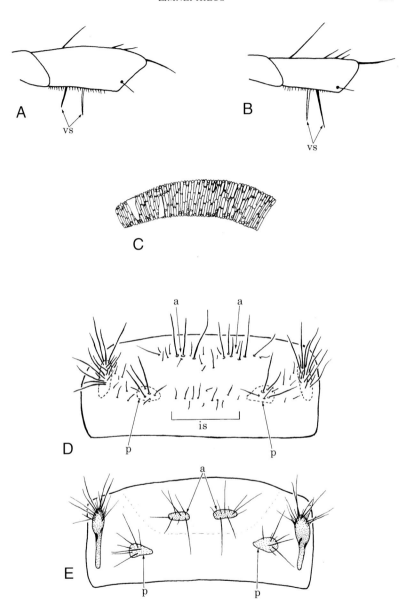

Fig. 85. **A, B:** femur of *Limnephilus sparsus*, posterior view: A, 2nd leg; B, 3rd leg. **C:** case of *L. sparsus*. **D, E:** metadorsum: D, *L. extricatus*; E, *L. griseus*.

63   Lateral sclerite of anal proleg with several squat, yellow or brown, setae *ss* on the face (Fig. 86A); (the squat setae are easily detached when adherent debris is removed, but their broad alveoli will be clearly visible)— **Rhadicoleptus alpestris** (Kolenati)

All sclerites pale golden brown with little darker pigmentation. Case made with small plant pieces arranged tangentially (as in Fig. 85C, p. 201).

Small, temporary, shallow peat pools among tussocks of vegetation, especially *Eriophorum vaginatum* L.; upland watershed bogs and lowland raised bogs. Wales and northern England, also Dumfries & Galloway and Speyside (Highland).

—   Lateral sclerite of anal proleg with no squat setae on the face (Fig. 86B)—   **64**

64   Lobe of anal proleg with setae *ls* on soft cuticle by the anal slit (as in Fig. 80A, p. 193). 9th abdominal dorsal sclerite with all setae, other than innermost primary setae *I*, less than half as long as outermost primary setae *O* (Fig. 86C)—   **Limnephilus vittatus** (Fabricius)

Central prosternite about twice as wide as it is high (Fig. 86D). Dorsal surface of head usually very dark brown, normally evenly coloured but posterior tip of fronto-clypeal apotome may be pale (as in Fig. 88D, p. 207). Case made with sand grains (Fig. 86E), anterior end typically notched in dorsal view (Fig. 86F).

Sandy or silty areas of lakes, ponds and temporary pools. Widespread and common.

—   Lobe of anal proleg with no setae on soft cuticle by the anal slit (as in Fig. 80B, p. 193). 9th abdominal dorsal sclerite with at least 1 seta, other than innermost primary setae *I*, which is more than half as long as outermost primary setae *O* (as in Figs 81F,G, p. 195)—   **65**

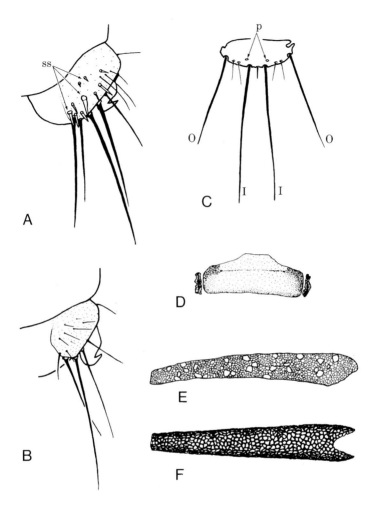

Fig. 86. **A, B:** right anal proleg, dorsal view: A, *Rhadicoleptus alpestris*; B, *Limnephilus centralis*. **C–F:** *Limnephilus vittatus*: C, 9th abdominal dorsal sclerite; D, prosternites; E, case, lateral view; F, case, dorsal view.

65 Central prosternite about twice as wide as it is high (Fig. 87A)—
Limnephilus centralis Curtis
Instars IV (some) and V

At instar V (headwidth 0.90–1.30 mm), 1st abdominal venter with 1–11 setae in each lateral setal group *l* (as in Fig. 87E) and lateral sclerite of anal proleg with 11–18 setae (including the 5 primary setae *P* along posterior edge, Fig. 87G). Head brown, usually with pale posterior tip to fronto-clypeal apotome (Fig. 89F, p. 209). Case made with sand grains (Fig. 87B) or occasionally with, or entirely of, small pieces of plant material.

Temporary pools and runnels on moorland; also in marshes, ditches and ponds. Widespread and common.

— Central prosternite about one-and-a-half times as wide as it is high (Fig. 87C) or not apparent— **66**

66 Headwidth more than 0.90 mm— **Limnephilus bipunctatus** Curtis

Headwidth at instar V more than 1.30 mm. At instar IV (headwidth 1.00–1.20 mm), 1st abdominal venter with 1–3 setae in each lateral group *l* (see Fig. 87E) and lateral sclerite of anal proleg with 8–11 setae (including the 5 primary setae *P* along posterior edge, see Fig. 87G). Head brown with a pale posterior tip to fronto-clypeal apotome and a pale area on posterior region of each parietal (as in Fig. 87F). Case made with small mineral particles, often embellished with fragments of decaying grass blades or roots (Fig. 87D), or partly or entirely built with small pieces of plant material.

Streams, ditches and pools which may dry up in summer. Throughout Britain; local.

— Headwidth less than 0.90 mm— **Limnephilus centralis** Curtis
Instar IV (some)

Temporary pools and runnels on moorland; also in marshes, ditches and ponds. Widespread and common.

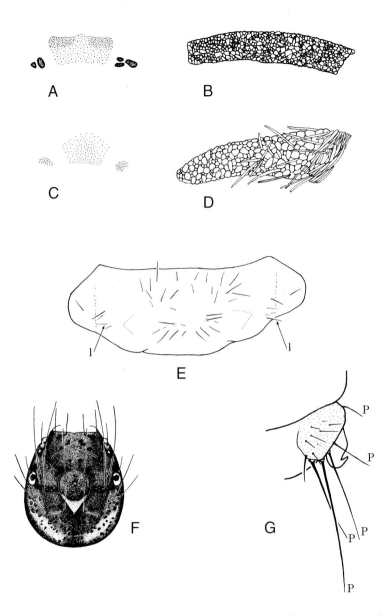

Fig. 87. **A, B:** *Limnephilus centralis*: A, prosternites; B, case. **C, D:** *L. bipunctatus*: C, prosternites; D, case. **E:** 1st abdominal segment, ventral view, of *L. affinis*. **F:** head capsule of *L. griseus*. **G:** right anal proleg, dorsal view, of *L. centralis*.

67(61) Anterior–lateral gills present on 2nd abdominal segment (see Fig. 4C, p. 18)—   **69**

— No anterior-lateral gills on 2nd abdominal segment—   **68**

68   Head with pale areas around edges of fronto-clypeal apotome (Figs 88A–C) and usually with distinct fronto-clypeal *fb* and parietal *pb* bands (Figs 88A,B). Distal section of trochanter of 2nd or 3rd leg, in anterior view, with 1 or more dark proximo-dorsal setae *as* between the 2 pale primary setae *ps* (Fig. 88E) or with additional setae *ds* arising dorsal to the suture (Fig. 88F)—   **Limnephilus lunatus** Curtis

1st abdominal venter with some setae in posterior *p* and lateral *l* setal groups arising from small pigmented patches (as in Fig. 94A, p. 219), most conspicuous at instar IV. Case variously made with plant material, mineral particles or a mixture (Fig. 88H); (if case is made with plant pieces arranged tangentially, or the prosternite is wider than it is high, see *L. rhombicus* via the first part of couplet 70, p. 210).

Among aquatic vegetation in all types of permanent waterbodies, but not in fast-flowing water. Widespread and common.

—   Head dark brown with no pale areas around edges of fronto-clypeal apotome, though posterior tip of apotome may be pale (Fig. 88D). Distal section of trochanters of 2nd and 3rd legs, in anterior view, with no dark proximo-dorsal setae between the 2 pale primary setae *ps* and with no additional setae arising dorsal to the suture (Fig. 88G)—
                                                Limnephilus auricula Curtis

1st abdominal venter with no setae arising from a pigmented patch. Metadorsum with anterior-median sclerites small, dark and clearly defined (if not, see *L. luridus*, couplet 82, p. 222). Case made with butted and overlapped plant pieces (as in Fig. 81C, p. 195).

Temporary grassy pools and ditches. Widespread and common.

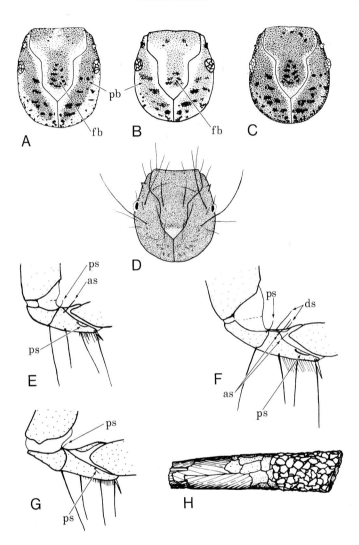

Fig. 88. **A–C:** head capsule of *Limnephilus lunatus*. **D:** head capsule of *L. auricula*. **E–G:** trochanter of 2nd leg, anterior view: E, *L. lunatus*, instar IV; F, *L. lunatus*, instar V; G, *L. auricula*. **H:** case of *L. lunatus*.

69(67) Head with fronto-clypeal *fb* and parietal *pb* bands comprising more or less uniform areas of dark colour, the pale ground colour being visible between the bands for most of their length (Figs 89A–D)—   **70**

—   Head without obvious fronto-clypeal and parietal bands, though there may be small pale areas around the edges of the fronto-clypeal apotome (Figs 89E–G)—   **78**

Fig. 89. **A–F:** head capsule: A, *Limnephilus decipiens*; B, *L. fuscinervis*; C, *L. binotatus*; D, *L. fuscinervis*, lateral view; E, *Grammotaulius nigropunctatus*; F, *L. centralis*. **G:** part of right side of head capsule of *L. luridus*, lateral view.

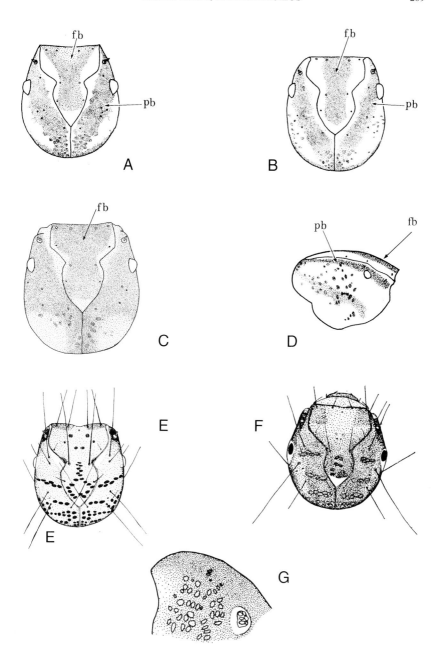

70   *EITHER:* proventer (see Fig. 3, p. 17) with large lateral sternites *l* that
are fused with the central prosternite *c* to give a single sclerite which is
at least twice as wide as it is high (Figs 90B,C,E) or lie very close to the
central prosternite (Fig. 90A), *OR:* case of plant pieces arranged
tangentially with both their ends protruding (as in Figs 90G,H); (larvae
with headwidths greater than 1.50 mm have both characters)—   **71**

Case construction often changes during instar V and full-grown larvae may have
cases made with chunks of plant material (Fig. 90I), mollusc shells, seeds or
mineral particles. Anterior one-third of pronotum always uniformly darker than
posterior two-thirds (as in Fig. 90F).

—   Proventer with small lateral sternites *l* lying a little apart from the central
prosternite (Fig. 90D) or with indistinct prosternites AND case of plant
pieces arranged longitudinally and often overlapping (e.g. Fig. 90J);
occasionally the case is triangular in cross-section (Fig. 90K)—   **74**

Do not continue with the key if the case is missing, the anterior third of the
pronotum is uniformly darker than the posterior two-thirds and the headwidth is
less than 1.50 mm; the larva is one of the following species: *Limnephilus
rhombicus, L. politus, L. binotatus, L. decipiens.*

Fig. 90. **A–D:** prosternites: A, B: *Limnephilus rhombicus*; C, *L. politus.* D, *L.
decipiens.* **E:** prosternite and prosternal horn of *L. rhombicus.* **F–H:** *L.
flavicornis:* F, pronotum; G, case and larva; H, transverse section of case.
I–K: cases: I, *L. rhombicus*; J, *L. binotatus*; K, *L. nigriceps,* triangular type
of case.

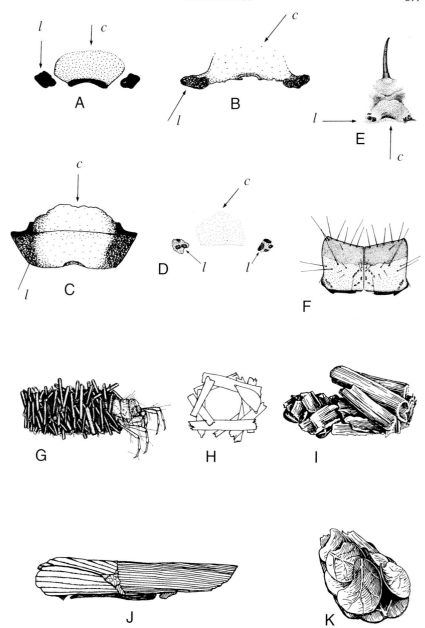

71   Headwidth more than 1.50mm—   **72**

—   Headwidth less than 1.50 mm—   **73**

72   Lateral prosternites *l* fused with central prosternite to give a single
      sclerite which is widest about halfway between the anterior and posterior
      edges; anterior edge of prosternite is well-defined (Figs 91D,E). Margin
      of prosternite anterior to the widest point is marked by a very dark patch
      of colour with a curved edge (*p* in Figs 91D,E)—
                                      Limnephilus politus McLachlan
                                      Instar V (about 5%)

      Lakes and canals. England, Wales and southern Scotland; generally local but
      commonest in southern England. Final-instar larvae are found during summer.

—   Lateral prosternites *EITHER* separate from central prosternite (Fig. 91A)
      OR fused with it to give a single sclerite that is widest close to its
      posterior margin (Figs 91B,C); anterior edge of prosternite often ill-
      defined. Margin of prosternite anterior to the widest point is not marked
      by a patch of very dark colour—   **Limnephilus rhombicus** (L.)
                                      Instar V

      Found in a wide range of still and slow to moderately flowing waters. Widespread
      and common. Final-instar larvae are found from autumn to early summer.

73   Lateral prosternites fused with central prosternite (Figs 91F,G). Any
      darkened area in the middle of the posterior margin of the central
      prosternite is narrow (*d* in Figs 91F,G)*—
                                      Limnephilus politus McLachlan
                                      Instar IV (over half)

      See couplet 72 for habitat and distribution.

—   Lateral prosternites separate from central prosternite (Figs 91H,I).
      Posterior margin of the central prosternite with a wide darkened area *d*;
      this may be the only part of the central prosternite that is apparent (Figs
      91H,I)*—   **Limnephilus rhombicus** (L.)
                                      Instar IV
      See couplet 72 for habitat and distribution.

      *If no part of the central prosternite is visible, the larva cannot be identified.

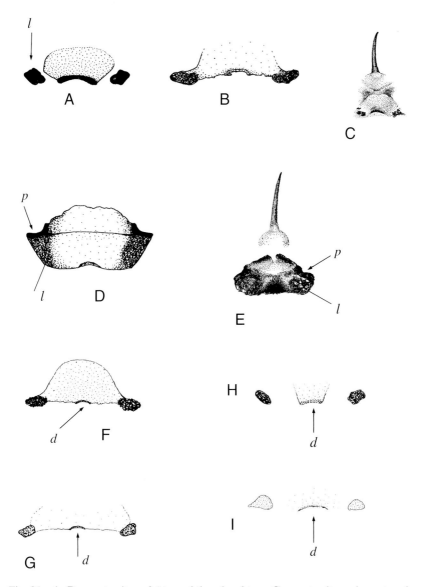

Fig. 91. **A, B:** prosternites of *Limnephilus rhombicus*. **C:** prosternite and prosternal horn of *L. rhombicus*. **D:** prosternite of *L. politus*. **E:** prosternite and prosternal horn of *L. politus*. **F, G:** prosternites of *L. politus* instar IV. **H, I:** prosternites of *L. rhombicus* instar IV.

74(70) Pleural band *plb* long and distinct, joining parietal band *pb* along the coronal suture (Figs 92A,B,D)—   **76**

—   Pleural band absent, indistinct or short and not joining parietal band along the coronal suture (Figs 92C,E and as in Fig. 92F)—   **75**

75   Lateral surface of head predominantly pale with strongly contrasting muscle attachment spots (Fig. 92E). Posterior region of parietal band lies well clear of fronto-clypeal suture (as in Fig. 92B, region arrowed)—
Limnephilus borealis (Zetterstedt)

Anterior edge of fronto-clypeal band *fb* narrow (as in Fig. 92B) or broad (as in Fig. 92A). Case long and slender, made with overlapping pieces of plant material (as in Fig. 93F, p. 217). Found during summer.

Lakes and pools; among plants or litter of *Carex* and *Phragmites*. Highland areas of Scotland; locally common.

—   Lateral surface of head predominantly brown, without strongly contrasting muscle attachment spots (as in Fig. 92F). Posterior region of parietal band touches fronto-clypeal suture (Fig. 92C, region arrowed)—
Limnephilus binotatus Curtis

Anterior edge of fronto-clypeal band *fb* always broad (Fig. 92C). Found from autumn to spring.

Case straight, made with butted and overlapped plant material (Fig. 90J, p. 211).

Among emergent vegetation in fens and lake margins in regions which lack standing water in summer. Widespread but local.

[NOTE: Some specimens of *L. binotatus* at instars IV and V will have keyed out at couplets 58 and 59 on pages 196 and 198].

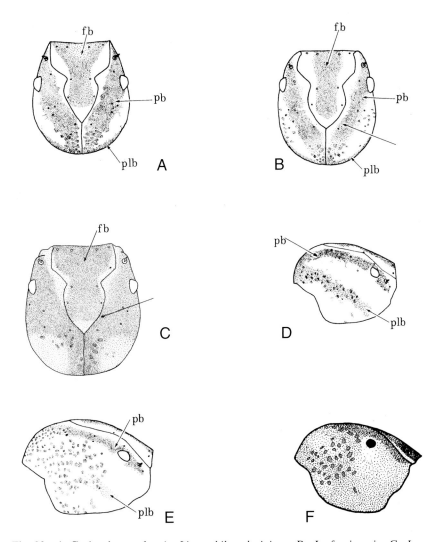

Fig. 92. **A–C:** head capsule: A, *Limnephilus decipiens*; B, *L. fuscinervis*; C, *L. binotatus*. **D–F:** head capsule, lateral view: D, *L. subcentralis*; E, *L. borealis*; F, *L. affinis*.

76(74) Posterior region of parietal band *pb* approaches or touches fronto-clypeal suture and slopes away again (arrow, Fig. 93A)—
Limnephilus decipiens (Kolenati)
(Some)

Anterior edge of fronto-clypeal band *fb* always broad (Fig. 93A). Femur of 1st leg with both ventral edge setae *vs* pale in colour (as in Fig. 69B, p. 173). Case made with butted or overlapped plant pieces, sometimes triangular in cross-section (as in Fig. 93E).

Lakes, canals and dykes with some vegetation. South-east and midland England north to Cheshire and Lincolnshire; locally common. Also in central Ireland.

— Posterior region of parietal band *pb* lies well clear of fronto-clypeal suture and runs more or less parallel to it (arrow, Fig. 93B)—   **77**

77 Muscle attachment spots between parietal band *pb* and pleural band *plb* are as dark as those in the bands (Figs 93B,D)—
Limnephilus fuscinervis (Zetterstedt)

Anterior edge of fronto-clypeal band *fb* narrow (Fig. 93B) or broad (as in Fig. 93A). Femur of 1st leg with ventral edge setae *vs* contrasting in colour (as in Fig. 69A, p. 173). Case long and slender, made with overlapping pieces of plant material (Fig. 93F).

Lakes and pools; among plants or litter of *Carex* and *Phragmites*. Central Ireland; locally common.

— Muscle attachment spots between parietal band *pb* and pleural band *plb* are absent or very much paler than those in the bands (Fig. 93C)—
Limnephilus subcentralis Brauer

Anterior edge of fronto-clypeal band *fb* narrow (as in Fig. 93B). Femur of 1st leg with ventral edge setae *vs* similar or contrasting in colour (as in Figs 69A,B, p. 173). Case long and slender, made with overlapping pieces of plant material (as in Fig. 93F).

Lakes and pools with emergent marginal vegetation. Southern and central highlands of Scotland.

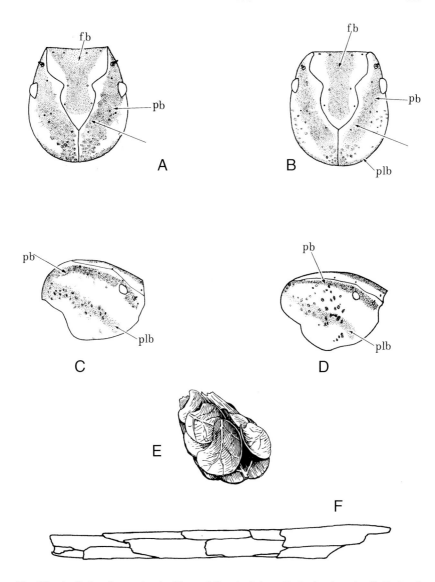

Fig. 93. **A, B:** head capsule: A, *Limnephilus decipiens*; B, *L. fuscinervis*. **C, D:** head capsule, lateral view: C, *L. subcentralis*; D, *L. fuscinervis*. **E, F:** case: E, *L. nigriceps*, triangular type; F, *L. fuscinervis*.

78(69) Headwidth more than 2.10 mm—
        Genus GRAMMOTAULIUS, instar V, **85**

—   Headwidth less than 2.10 mm—   **79**

79   Headwidth more than 1.20 mm—   **80**

—   Headwidth less than 1.20 mm—   **81**

80   1st abdominal venter with 13–36 setae in anterior setal groups *a*, both
        groups included (Fig. 94A). Mesonotum with 8–21 setae in each
        anterior-median area *am* (see Fig. 94B)—   (instar V), **82**

        Distal section of trochanters of 2nd and 3rd legs, in anterior view, with no dark
        proximo-dorsal setae between the two pale primary setae *ps* and with no
        additional setae arising dorsal to the suture (as in Fig. 94E).

—   1st abdominal venter with 2–12 (exceptionally up to 14) setae in anterior
        setal groups *a*, both groups included. Mesonotum with 1–8 setae in each
        anterior-median area—   **83**

        Distal section of trochanter of 2nd or 3rd leg, in anterior view, frequently with 1
        or more dark proximo-dorsal setae *as* between the 2 pale primary setae *ps* or with
        additional setae *ds* arising dorsal to the suture (as in Figs 94C,D). Each side of
        9th abdominal dorsal sclerite with all setae between innermost primary seta *I* and
        outermost primary seta *O* less than half as long as seta *O* (Fig. 95E, p. 221).

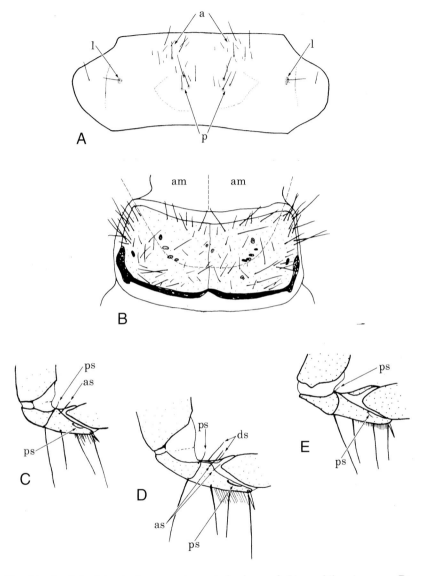

Fig. 94. **A:** 1st abdominal segment, ventral view, of *Limnephilus ignavus*. **B:** mesonotum of *L. extricatus*. **C–E:** trochanter of 2nd leg, anterior view: C, *L. lunatus*, instar IV; D, *L. lunatus*, instar V; E, *L. auricula*.

81(79) 1st abdominal venter with 5–18 setae in anterior setal groups a, both groups included (see Fig. 94A, p. 219). Mesonotum with 3–10 setae in each anterior-median area am (see Fig. 94B)—   (instar IV), **82**

Distal section of trochanters of 2nd and 3rd legs, in anterior view, with no dark proximo-dorsal setae between the two pale primary setae ps (as in Fig. 94E).

—   1st abdominal venter with 2–4 setae in anterior setal groups a, both groups included. Mesonotum with 1–3 setae in each anterior-median area—   **83**

Distal section of trochanter of 2nd or 3rd leg frequently with 1 or more dark proximo-dorsal setae as between the two pale primary setae ps (as in Fig. 94C). Each side of 9th abdominal dorsal sclerite with all setae between innermost primary seta I and outermost primary seta O less than half as long as seta O (as in Fig. 95C).

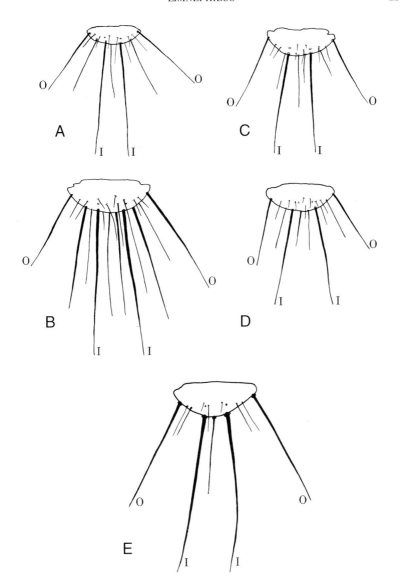

Fig. 95. **A, B:** 9th abdominal dorsal sclerite of *L. luridus*: A, instar IV; B, instar V. **C, D:** 9th abdominal dorsal sclerite of *L. ignavus*. **E:** 9th abdominal dorsal sclerite of *L. binotatus*.

82(80,81) Each side of 9th abdominal dorsal sclerite with at least 1 seta between innermost primary seta *I* and outermost primary seta *O* which is three-quarters or more of the length of seta *O* at instar IV (Fig. 95A, p. 221) and equal to seta *O* at instar V (Fig. 95B). Lateral sclerite of anal proleg with 1 seta (arrow, Figs 96A,B) next to innermost seta *iP* of the five primary setae *P* which is more than half as long as seta *iP* (Figs 96A,B). Metadorsum with anterior-median sclerites *a* ill-defined (Fig. 96D) and paler than the mesonotum —   **Limnephilus luridus** Curtis

Head reddish-brown with slightly paler muscle attachment spots (Fig. 96F). Case made with butted and overlapped pieces of plant material, smooth and slightly barrel-shaped when full-sized (Fig. 96H).

Acidic, usually temporary, pools with much dead plant material. Widespread and common.

—   Each side of 9th abdominal dorsal sclerite with all setae between innermost primary seta *I* and outermost primary seta *O* less than half as long as seta *O* at instar IV and no more than three-quarters as long as seta *O* at instar V (Figs 95C,D). Lateral sclerite of anal proleg with all setae next to innermost seta *iP* of the five primary setae *P* less than half as long as seta *iP* (Fig. 96C). Metadorsum with anterior-median sclerites *a* small, clearly defined (Fig. 96E) and as dark as the mesonotum —
                Limnephilus ignavus McLachlan

Head dark brown with even darker muscle attachment spots (Fig. 96G). 1st abdominal venter with some setae in posterior *p* and lateral *l* setal groups arising from small pigmented areas (Fig. 94A, p. 219); if not, see *L. auricula*, couplet 68, p. 206). Case made with butted and overlapped pieces of plant material (as in Fig. 81C, p. 195).

Shallow pools and marshes with flowing water. Widespread but local; most frequent in Scotland.

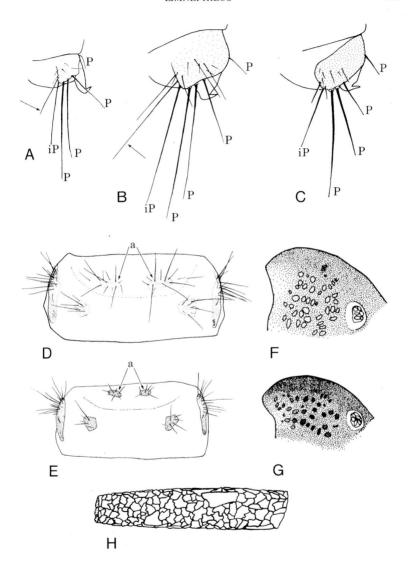

Fig. 96. **A–C:** right anal proleg, dorsal view: A, *Limnephilus luridus*, instar IV; B, *L. luridis*, instar V; C, *L. ignavus*. **D, E:** metadorsum: D, *L. luridus*; E, *L. ignavus*. **F, G:** part of right side of head capsule, lateral view: F, *L. luridus*; G, *L. ignavus*. **H:** case of *L. luridus*.

83(80,81) Gill(s) present on 8th abdominal segment—   **84**

—   No gills on 8th abdominal segment—   **86**

84   Headwidth more than 1.30 mm—
                                    Genus GRAMMOTAULIUS, instar IV, **85**

—   Headwidth less than 1.30 mm—   **Limnephilus binotatus** Curtis
                                                        Instar IV (some)

See the second part of couplet 58 on p. 196 for additional information.

85(78,84) Femora of 2nd and 3rd legs with all ventral edge setae *vs* dark in
colour and similar in size (Figs 97A,B)—
                          Grammotaulius nigropunctatus (Retzius)

Head brown, often with small pale areas around edges of fronto-clypeal apotome
(Fig. 97E). At instar IV, 9th abdominal dorsal sclerite has 8–9 setae, as in Fig.
86C, p. 203 (if there are 10–16, see *L. binotatus*, couplet 58, p. 196). Distal
region of trochanters of 2nd and 3rd legs with a ventral row of long flexuous
spines *lp* (as in Fig. 97G; if spines are dagger-like (*dp* in Fig. 97H), see *L.
elegans*, couplet 86, p. 226). Gills almost always present at two or more sites on
8th abdominal segment. Case made with overlapped pieces of plant material
(Fig. 97F), often much longer than the larva.

Among emergent vegetation in pools and ditches which may dry up during
summer. Widespread and common.

—   Femora of 2nd and 3rd legs with ventral edge setae *vs* contrasting in
colour and size (Figs 97C,D)—   **Grammotaulius nitidus** (Müller)

(Based on a description by Lepneva 1971).

Head pattern and case similar to those of *G. nigropunctatus*.

No larvae are known from Britain or Ireland; in the Soviet Union they have been
found in small overgrown waterbodies, especially swampy pools which dry up
in summer. There are old records of adults from Kent, the Somerset Levels,
Cambridgeshire Fens, and the Norfolk and Suffolk Broads.

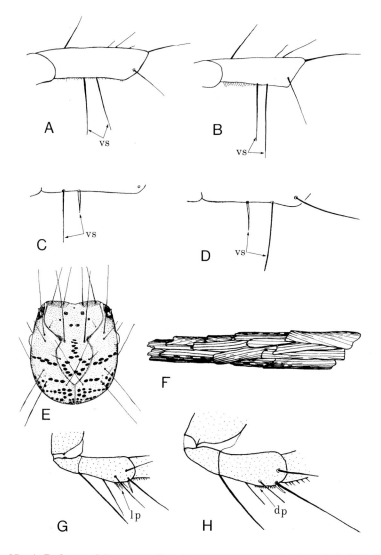

Fig. 97. **A, B:** femur of *Grammotaulius nigropunctatus*, posterior view: A, 2nd leg; B, 3rd leg. **C, D:** ventral edge of femur of *G. nitidus*, posterior view: C, 2nd leg; D, 3rd leg. **E:** head capsule of *G. nigropunctatus*. **F:** case of *G. nigropunctatus*. **G, H:** trochanter of 3rd leg, posterior view: G, *Limnephilus binotatus*, instar IV; H, *L. elegans*.

86(83) Head with pale areas around edges of fronto-clypeal apotome (Fig. 98A)—   **Limnephilus binotatus** Curtis
(Some)

Distal region of trochanters of 2nd and, usually, 3rd legs with a ventral row of long flexuous spines *lp* (Fig. 98D). See the second part of couplet 58 on p. 196 for more information.

—   Head without pale areas around edges of fronto-clypeal apotome, though posterior tip of apotome may be pale (as in Fig. 98B)—
Limnephilus elegans (Curtis)

Distal region of trochanters of 2nd and 3rd legs with a ventral row of short dagger-like spines *dp* and no long flexuous spines (Fig. 98E; if not, see *L. borealis*, couplet 75, p. 214). Head brown. Case usually made with overlapped pieces of plant material (as in Fig. 98C) at instar V, but at instar IV it may be made with cut pieces of root arranged in a spiral, resembling Fig. 102A, p. 237.

Small pools on raised bogs and in acid fens. Widespread but local.

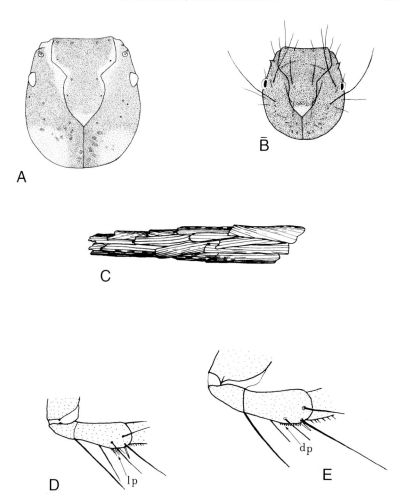

Fig. 98. **A, B:** head capsule: A, *Limnephilus binotatus*; B, *L. auricula*. **C:** case of *Grammotaulius nigropunctatus*. **D, E:** trochanter of 3rd leg, posterior view: D, *L. binotatus*; E, *L. elegans*.

KEY TO FAMILY MOLANNIDAE
(ONE GENUS AND TWO SPECIES)

Both British species (Table 9) live in still or slow-flowing water on a substratum of sand or fine gravel. They have distinctive cases of sand grains cemented together to form a convex shield-shaped plate incorporating a central tube (Figs 99F–H). The wings of the plate extend forwards as a hood covering the anterior opening of the tube (Fig. 99F); (the lateral wings are easily damaged and may be accidentally broken off during sampling and sorting). The cases are very well camouflaged against the bare substrata on which the larvae often live. They are only conspicuous when the larvae move, which they do in jerks achieved by bounding leaps.

Molannid larvae are characterised by the presence of numerous spines on the tarsal claw of the third leg. This unique feature is easily seen at the final instar (Figs 99A,C) but at early instars the spines are short (Figs 99B,D) and the slender claw might be mistaken, at low magnification, for a normal claw. Another notable feature, on the tibia of the first leg, is the presence of an obvious ventral process bearing a single stout seta (Fig. 11E, p. 35); (a process is also present on the tibia of the second leg). Molannids have moderately long antennae arising close to the anterior margin of the head capsule and may possibly be misidentified as leptocerids (Key to Families, couplet 8, p. 32). However, the antenna is broad at the base (arrow, Fig. 99E), and even at instar II the length/width ratio does not exceed 4.

Molanna angustata has a long flight period (May to September) and instars III–V have been found in winter. *M. albicans* has a short flight period in late summer and overwinters as young larvae (Leader 1968); Mr R. A. Jenkins has collected instars II and III at the end of April.

Table 9. Headwidths of Molannidae: ranges (mm) (and *n*) for instars II to V.

Species	Instar II	Instar III	Instar IV	Instar V
Molanna albicans	0.31 (1)	0.43–0.45 (5)	—	0.90–1.02 (4)
Molanna angustata	0.30–0.32 (7)	0.41–0.49 (10)	0.57–0.77 (13)	0.90–1.15 (10)

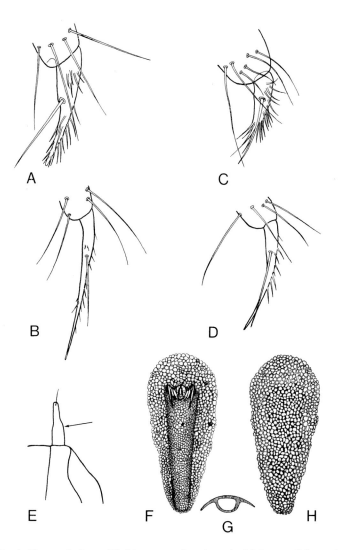

Fig. 99. **A–D:** tarsal claw of 3rd leg, posterior view: A, *Molanna albicans*, instar V; B, *M. albicans*, instar III; C, *M. angustata,* instar V; D, *M. angustata*, instar III. **E:** anterior-lateral region of head capsule of *M. angustata*, instar II. **F–H:** case of *M. angustata*: F, ventral view; G, transverse section; H, dorsal view.

KEY TO LARVAE

1   Dorsal surface of anal proleg lateral sclerite with one long, curved, thick
     seta *ss* (Fig. 100A). Posterior part of fronto-clypeal apotome dark (arrow,
     Fig. 100C)—   **Molanna albicans** (Zetterstedt)

     Small upland lakes in Wales, lakes in central and northern Scotland, lakes and
     slow-flowing rivers in central Ireland. Local.

—   Dorsal surface of anal proleg lateral sclerite with several shorter, thick
     setae *ss* (Fig. 100B). Posterior part of fronto-clypeal apotome pale
     (arrow, Fig. 100D)—   **Molanna angustata** Curtis

     England north to Cumbria and Yorkshire, and a few Welsh records; often
     common in lakes, pools, slow-flowing rivers and canals.

     NOTE: these two species have not been found co-existing in Britain.

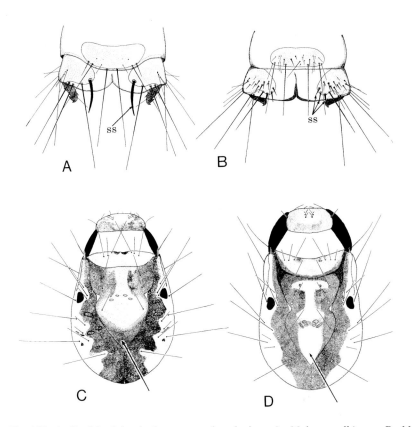

Fig. 100. **A, B:** 9th abdominal segment, dorsal view: A, *Molanna albicans*; B, *M. angustata*. **C:** head of *M. albicans*. **D:** head *of M. angustata*.

KEY TO FAMILY ODONTOCERIDAE
(ONE GENUS AND SPECIES)

Odontocerum albicorne (Scopoli) is the only British representative of this family. It is a common species, widespread in stony streams and rivers. The larvae are omnivorous scavengers, most active at night (Elliott 1970).

The case is curved and composed of sand grains (Fig. 101C). Its construction differs from that of other caddis cases, in which building materials are joined together around an internal silken tube. In the case of *O. albicorne*, each sand grain is carefully mortared to its neighbours with silk and the joints are reinforced internally with silken braces (Fig. 101F). The resultant case is very strong and rigid, and snaps without first deforming if subjected to bending stress. The posterior end of the case is also distinctive, the opening being protected by a pebble (Fig. 101D). Before pupating the larva also protects the anterior opening of the case with a pebble (Fig. 101E).

The larvae are readily recognisable at instars IV and V by the presence of a distinctive but somewhat variable anchor-shaped mark on the fronto-clypeal apotome (Fig. 14I, p. 41) and the arrangement of sclerites on the metadorsum (Fig. 101A). At instars II and III the fronto-clypeal mark is absent or indistinct and the posterior metadorsal sclerite is ill-defined (Fig. 101B). These small larvae might be mistaken for sericostomatids but are distinguished by the characteristic anal proleg claw (Fig. 14H) which has a gently curved crook and lacks accessory hooks, and by the presence on the anal proleg of no more than five setae (excluding those on the claw, Figs 14E,F). *Odontocerum albicorne* and *Sericostoma personatum* are often found together under stones.

The life cycle of *O. albicorne* in a small stream in the English Lake District has been studied by Elliott (1982). The species was univoltine, with five larval instars. Consideration of the headwidths of prepupae, sex of pupae and case lengths revealed two distinct size groups within instar V, smaller and larger groups corresponding to future male and female pupae respectively (Table 10). The larvae overwintered mainly in instars III or V. Larvae in instar III grew rapidly in spring to form the 'female' group in instar V. The flight period is between early summer and autumn.

Table 10. Headwidths of Odontoceridae: ranges (mm) (and *n*) at instars II to V of *Odontocerum albicorne*. (After Elliott 1982).

Instar II	Instar III	Instar IV	Instar V male	Instar V female
0.35–0.60 (86)	0.65–0.85 (313)	0.90–1.35 (256)	1.40–1.65 (207)	1.70–2.10 (107)

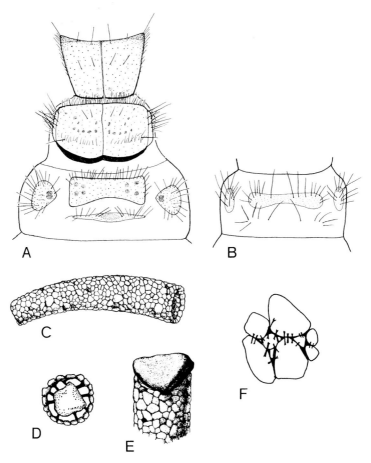

Fig. 101. *Odontocerum albicorne*. **A**: thorax, dorsal view. **B**: metathorax, dorsal view, instar II. **C, D**: case: C, lateral view; D, posterior end. **E**: anterior end of pupal case. **F**: part of interior surface of case showing silken braces.

KEY TO FAMILY PHRYGANEIDAE
(SIX GENERA AND TEN SPECIES)

Phryganeid larvae live in tubular cases made from pieces of plant stem or leaves. Some species are very large, reaching 40 mm in length when full-grown. Most have conspicuously banded heads (e.g. Figs 104A,C,E, p. 241) and spirally whorled cases (Fig. 102B, p. 237), though the spiral may not be obvious in the early-instar case (Fig. 102A). All are readily recognisable by the presence of prominent lateral protuberances on the first abdominal segment, *and* the mesodorsum and metadorsum being largely unsclerotized and resembling each other in setal arrangement (Fig. 7H, p. 27).

Larvae are encountered in a wide variety of still and slow-flowing waters, such as ponds, lakes, bogs and canals. Most species reach the final instar during spring and early summer. Bray (1966) summarised the distribution of the ten British species in the Family; the most important additional records given here concern *Trichostegia minor* and *Hagenella clathrata*. Headwidths of larvae are given in Table 11.

Larvae of this family often leave their cases when disturbed, in contrast to other tube-cased caddis which are reluctant to do so; they also re-enter them more readily. The full-grown larva of *Agrypnia pagetana* frequently utilises a piece of hollow stem of reed or horsetail as its case. Some species have the unusual habit of adding length to the case just before pupation; the majority of caddis shorten the case at that time.

Arrangement of coxal combs

The arrangement of the coxal combs (comb-like spines on the coxae, e.g. Figs 105A–E, p. 243) is used at several points in the following key. These combs are not always easy to see and are especially difficult at instar III and in long-preserved larvae, where the combs are very similar in colour to the coxae. It is advisable to identify phryganeid larvae within a few months after preservation when this feature is at its most conspicuous. Combs are best seen with the coxa inclined at an angle of about 45 degrees to the vertical and using a magnification of at least x50; side illumination may also assist.

Table 11. Headwidths of Phryganeidae: ranges (mm) for instars II to V. Measurements were taken from several sources in addition to those of the authors; the number examined was not recorded.

*Not keyed to species at this instar.

Species	Instar II	Instar III	Instar IV	Instar V
Agrypnetes				
crassicornis	0.59–0.74	0.85–1.15	1.33–1.78	1.96–2.55
Agrypnia obsoleta	*0.48–0.59	0.74–0.92	1.04–1.40	1.52–2.08
Agrypnia pagetana	0.48–0.55	0.66–0.85	1.00–1.18	1.44–2.02
Agrypnia picta	—	—	—	1.45–2.15
Agrypnia varia	*0.42–0.55	0.67–0.81	1.03–1.34	1.52–2.12
Hagenella clathrata	0.68	0.86	1.16–1.36	1.76–2.28
Oligotricha striata	0.44–0.55	0.66–0.81	1.07–1.29	1.55–2.07
Phryganea				
bipunctata	*0.55–0.70	0.85–1.09	1.29–1.66	1.93–2.66
Phryganea grandis	* —	—	—	2.44–2.60
Trichostegia minor	0.40	0.52–0.54	0.84–0.91	1.13–1.44

KEY TO LARVAE

1   1st abdominal segment with dorsal and lateral protuberances (Fig. 103A, p. 239)—   **2**

—   1st abdominal segment with only lateral protuberances (Fig. 102C)—
      Trichostegia minor (Curtis)

Fronto-clypeal *fb* and parietal *pb* bands broad, often abutting for much of their length (Fig. 102D); head paler without bands at instar II. Pronotum dark, without conspicuous pale bands. Case made with pieces of dead leaves arranged longitudinally but not in a spiral (Fig. 102C).

Woods and fens; found over winter in stagnant leaf-filled pools and ditches which dry up or considerably diminish during summer. England; also a few sites in east Wales.

2   Dorsal surface of head and pronotum largely plain brown without conspicuous dark bands (Figs 102E,F). On 1st leg, apical seta of tibia and basal seta of tarsal claw are slightly curved, lie close to the leg and do not arise from a prominence (arrows, Fig. 102G)—
      Hagenella clathrata (Kolenati)

Case slightly curved, made with rectangular pieces of dead leaves joined end-to-end in uniform rings.

Shallow water-filled hollows among tussocks of grasses and sedges. Very rare and decreasing; recent records from bogs on the Wrexham/Shropshire border, Staffordshire, Surrey and Aviemore (Highland).

—   Dorsal surface of head and pronotum yellow or brown with conspicuous dark bands (Figs 103A,B, p. 239, 104A,C,E, p. 241). On 1st leg, apical seta of tibia and basal seta of tarsal claw are straight, do not lie close to the leg, and arise from a prominence (arrows, Fig. 102H)—   **3**

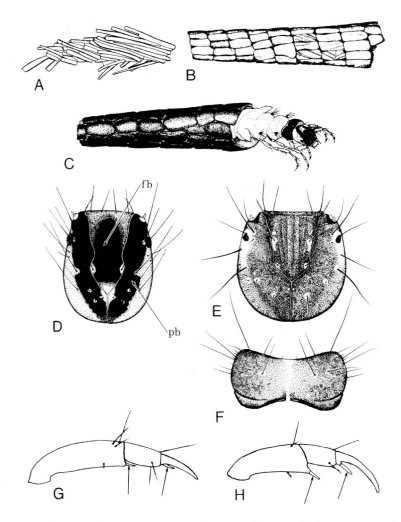

Fig. 102. **A:** case of *Agrypnia obsoleta*, instar III. **B:** case of *Phryganea grandis*, instar V. **C, D:** *Trichostegia minor*: C, larva in case; D, head capsule. **E–G:** *Hagenella clathrata*: E, head capsule; F, pronotum; G, tibia and tarsus of 1st leg, anterior view. **H:** tibia and tarsus of 1st leg, anterior view, of *Agrypnia varia*.

3   Parietal bands *pb* almost parallel, continuous posteriorly with
     longitudinal dark bands or patches on dorsum of thoracic and abdominal
     segments (Fig. 103A); fronto–clypeal band absent—
                                                       Oligotricha striata (L.)

     Deep pools and ditches, particularly those with acid peaty water. Common in
     Scotland and northern England, rare elsewhere in Britain; no recent Irish records.

—   Parietal bands *pb* converging towards coronal suture (Figs 103B,
     104A,C,E, p. 241), no longitudinal dark bands or patches on dorsum of
     thoracic or abdominal segments; fronto-clypeal band *fb* present (Figs
     103B; 104A,C,E)—   **4**

4   Parietal bands *pb* short, extending anteriorly only to eyes (Fig. 103B).
     Anal proleg with a gill-like process near its base (arrow, Fig. 103C) at
     instars III–V (headwidth more than 0.80 mm). (The gill-like process is
     only easy to see in fully-fed final-instar larvae)—
                                         Agrypnetes crassicornis (McLachlan)

     Case first built with fragments of *Chara* arranged spirally; later, pieces of leaf
     are used and the spiral pattern is less obvious. Known only from Malham Tarn,
     North Yorkshire.

—   Parietal bands *pb* long, extending anteriorly to bases of mandibles (Figs
     104A,C,E). Anal proleg without a gill-like process near its base—   **5**

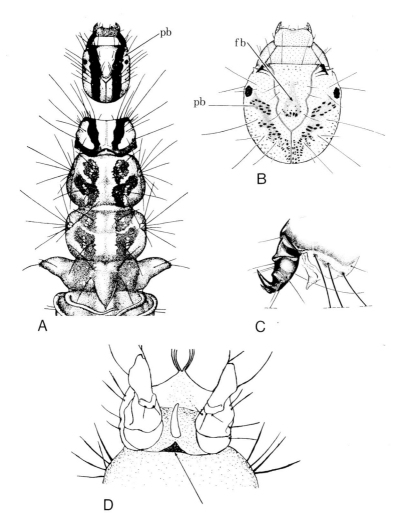

Fig. 103. **A:** head, thorax and 1st abdominal segment, dorsal view, of *Oligotricha striata*. **B, C:** *Agrypnetes crassicornis*: B, head; C, left anal proleg, dorsal view. **D:** prothorax, ventral view, of *Agrypnia obsoleta*.

5   Prosternite present (arrow, Fig. 103D, p. 239); (it may be hidden in the intersegmental fold, so the larva must be stretched to ensure this does not happen; the prosternite is also often very pale at instar II). Ventral surface of coxa of 2nd leg with some combs attached longitudinally (*lc*, Figs 105C,E, p. 243)—   Genus AGRYPNIA, **6**

—   Prosternite absent. Ventral surface of coxa of 2nd leg with all combs attached transversely (as in Figs 106A,B, p. 245)—
                                             Genus PHRYGANEA, **8**

Phryganea species are not separable at instar II: headwidth less than 0.75 mm, mesodorsum and metadorsum with only 1 seta at each anterior-lateral position.

6   Anterior margin of pronotum with a continuous transverse black band (as in Fig. 104B)—   (*Agrypnia obsoleta* and *A. varia*), **7**

These two species are not separable at instar II: headwidth less than 0.65 mm, mesodorsum and metadorsum with only 1 seta at each anterior-lateral position).

—   Anterior margin of pronotum with two discrete patches of pigment (Fig. 104D)—   **Agrypnia pagetana** Curtis
                                             Agrypnia picta Kolenati

These species may be separated on two characters. The fronto-clypeal band *fb* in *A. pagetana* is either of uniform width or widens slightly posteriorly (Fig. 104C) while in *A. picta* it is keyhole-shaped, widening markedly both anteriorly and posteriorly from a central constriction (Fig. 104E); Solem (1971) suggests that this difference will apply at instars II–V. The prosternite is dark in *A. pagetana* whilst in *A. picta* it is pale but has a bow-shaped posterior band which is usually very dark. (Characters for *A. picta* come from foreign material).

A. pagetana is a lowland species found in ponds, lakes and canals with emergent vegetation. It is widely distributed but is not recorded from northern Scotland. There are only two adult records of *A. picta*, both from the last century, and no specimens exist to confirm either record; its status as a British species is very suspect.

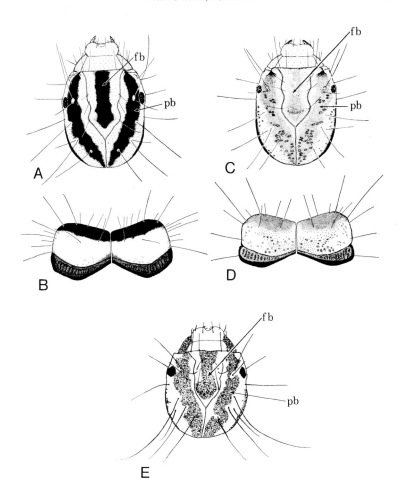

Fig. 104. **A, B:** *Phryganea bipunctata*: A, head; B, pronotum. **C, D:** *Agrypnia pagetana*: C, head; D, pronotum. **E:** head of *A. picta*.

7   Coxal combs of 1st and 2nd legs cover a broad area of the ventral surface
      (Figs 105B,C); on 2nd leg, combs are attached longitudinally or at an
      angle intermediate between longitudinal and transverse (Fig. 105C);
      (rarely, a few extreme distal combs are transversely attached)—

Agrypnia obsoleta (Hagen)

Instars III to V

At instar V, sometimes earlier, 7th abdominal segment has at least one dorsal gill
and 8th abdominal segment normally has an anterior-lateral gill.

Found in a variety of permanent, still waters. Common; mainly upland areas in
Scotland, northern England and Wales, more widespread in Ireland.

—   Coxal combs of 1st and 2nd legs form a narrow band on the ventral
      surface (Figs 105D,E); on 2nd leg, combs are attached transversely,
      longitudinally, and at intermediate angles (Fig. 105E)—

Agrypnia varia (Fabricius)

Instars III to V

7th abdominal segment with no dorsal gills; no gills on 8th abdominal segment.

Found in a variety of permanent, still waters. Widespread and common. Often
replaced by *A. obsoleta* in upland waters.

Fig. 105. **A:** 1st leg, posterior view, of *Agrypnia obsoleta*. **B–E:** right coxa, ventral
      view, showing arrangement of coxal combs: B, *A. obsoleta*, 1st leg; C, *A.
      obsoleta*, 2nd leg; D, *A. varia*, 1st leg; E, *A. varia*, 2nd leg.

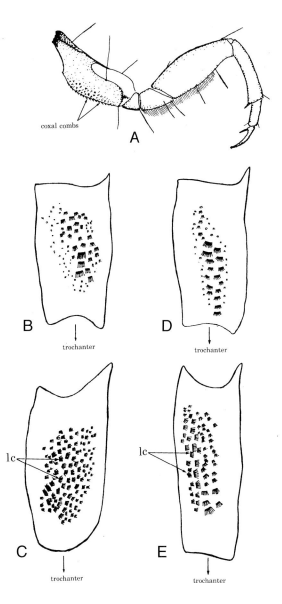

coxal combs

A

B

trochanter

D

trochanter

lc

C

trochanter

lc

E

trochanter

8(5) Well-developed coxal combs of 1st and 2nd legs arranged in 2–4 more
      or less regular longitudinal rows (Fig. 106A)—
                                                Phryganea bipunctata Retzius
                                                            Instars III to V

At instars IV and V, a mid-anterior pale patch on the labrum* does not extend
back to the level of the two face setae and has a length:width ratio of about 1:4
(Fig. 106C).

Ponds, lakes and canals. Widespread and common.

—   Well–developed coxal combs of 1st and 2nd legs arranged in 4 or more
      irregular longitudinal rows (Fig. 106B)—   **Phryganea grandis** L.
                                                            Instars III to V

At instars IV and V, a mid-anterior pale patch on the labrum* extends back to
the level of the two face setae and has a length:width ratio of about 1:2 (Fig.
106D).

Ponds, lakes and canals in lowland areas. Widespread. (There are numerous
records of adults but the larvae are rarely encountered).

* NOTE: This pale patch is difficult to distinguish in larvae that have been
preserved for a long period of time.

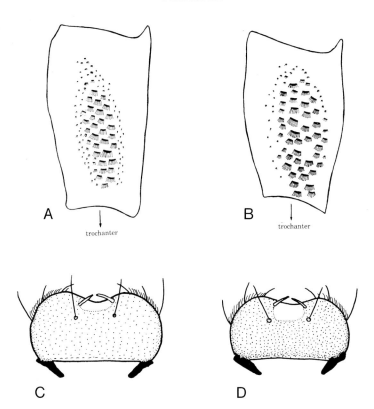

Fig. 106. **A, B:** coxa of 1st right leg, ventral view, showing arrangement of coxal combs: A, *Phryganea bipunctata*; B, *P. grandis*. **C:** labrum of *P. bipunctata*. **D:** labrum of *P. grandis*.

A key to the Family Sericostomatidae begins on page 247.

KEY TO FAMILY SERICOSTOMATIDAE
(TWO GENERA AND TWO SPECIES)

There are two British sericostomatids. The case of both species is curved and composed of sand grains (Fig. 107A, p. 249), and is closed at the posterior end by a slightly conical membrane with a central hole (Fig. 107B).

The dorsal surface of the head has a flattened appearance and is dark brown in large larvae; very early instars have pale heads. The metadorsum has pale or colourless sclerites which, together with their associated setae, form two parallel transverse bands (Figs 15G,H, p. 42). This resembles the arrangement in *Odontocerum albicorne,* a species often found with *Sericostoma personatum.* Moreover, the anterior-lateral corner of the pronotum is sharply pointed in both species at later instars. Sericostomatids can be readily separated from *O. albicorne* by the form of the anal proleg claw, which has accessory hooks and a sharply angled crook (Figs 14C,D, p. 41), and, except at instar II, by the presence of more than five setae on the anal proleg (excluding those on the claw, Figs 14A,B). In addition, the protrochantin is large with a hook-shaped tip (Figs 15B,C).

Small sericostomatid larvae superficially resemble the beraeid species *Beraea maurus, B. pullata* and *Ernodes articularis* in the form of the case and the shape and colour of the head. However, the anal proleg has no ventral brush of setae (compare Figs 12F and 12H, p. 37) or dorsal process and there is neither a sharp ridge nor a flap-like extension on the pronotum.

In Sericostomatidae, the number of larval instars appears to be variable. Elliott (1969) found six larval instars in *S. personatum* but Nielsen (1942) reported seven for the same species (as *S. pedemontanum* McLachlan). Resh *et al.* (1981) were able to induce up to fourteen instars in the North American sericostomatid *Gumaga nigricula* (McLachlan). The headwidths of full-grown British sericostomatid larvae are about 1.5 mm in *N. ciliaris* and 2.0 mm in *S. personatum.*

Notidobia ciliaris flies in May and final-instar larvae are found over winter. *Sericostoma personatum* has a more complicated life cycle (which has been studied by Elliott 1969) and final-instar larvae may be present during much of the year.

KEY TO LARVAE

1   Headwidth more than 0.25 mm —   **2**

—   Headwidth less than 0.25 mm —   **Notidobia ciliaris** (L.)
                                                   Sericostoma personatum (Spence)
                                                                    Instar II (?)

2   Anterior-lateral corner of pronotum either prolonged (Fig. 107C) or
     angular (Figs 107D,E), never smoothly rounded. Ridge (arrow, Fig.
     107G) on lateral margin of dorsal surface of head is restricted to anterior
     region close to the eye—   **Sericostoma personatum** (Spence)
                                                        Instar III (?) to Final instar

     Stony substratum in streams, rivers and lakes; also occasionally in spring
     streams and trickles. Widespread and common.

—   Anterior-lateral corner of pronotum smoothly rounded at all instars (Fig.
     107F). Ridge (arrow, Fig. 107H) on lateral margin of dorsal surface of
     head continues posteriorly to the coronal suture—
                                                            Notidobia ciliaris (L.)
                                                        Instar III (?) to Final instar

     Associated with submerged roots of marginal vegetation in slow-flowing water.
     Found in England as far north as the Shropshire/Wrexham border and
     Nottinghamshire; local.

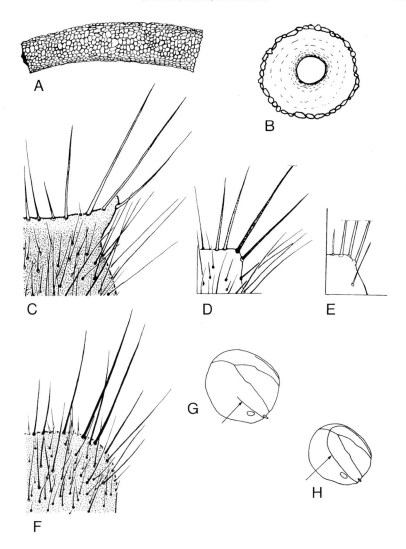

Fig. 107. **A, B:** case of *Sericostoma personatum*: A, lateral view; B, posterior end.
C–E: right anterior-lateral corner of pronotum of *S. personatum*: C, final
instar; D, early-instar larva of headwidth 0.55 mm; E, early-instar larva of
headwidth 0.30 mm. **F:** right anterior-lateral corner of pronotum of *Notidobia
ciliaris*. **G, H:** head capsule, dorso-lateral view: G, *S. personatum*; H, *N.
ciliaris*.

ACKNOWLEDGEMENTS

We would like to thank those who have provided specimens or commented upon earlier versions of the keys, in particular Dr P. C. Barnard, Mr J. Blackburn, Dr L. Botosaneanu, Dr M. I. Crichton, Mr D. A. Cooling, Dr V. Edmonds-Brown, Miss S. Eldin, Mr G. Fretwell, Dr G. M. Gislason, Dr D. Harding, Professor A. G. Hildrew, Dr P. D. Hiley, Mr R. A. Jenkins, Dr J. P. O'Connor, Mrs M. Spirit, Professor G. B. Wiggins and Dr N. E. Williams.

Distribution records were extracted from the Scottish Insect Published Records Index at the National Museum of Scotland and the collections of the following Museums: The Natural History Museum, Coventry, Liverpool, Manchester, National Museum of Scotland, Sheffield.

Professor R. B. Clark provided facilities for GNP at the University of Newcastle upon Tyne.

We are grateful to the authors and publishers of the following publications for permission to reproduce some of their drawings as the figures listed: Barnard (1971) 32D,E; Bray (1967) 103B, 104A–D, 105A, 106C,D (both modified); Edington & Hildrew (1995) 6A,C, 9A,B (all modified); Gislason (1979) 104E; Giudicelli & Vaillant (1967) 32F,J–L (all modified); Hickin (1967) 10D, 11F, 16A,C, 17A, 19C (modified), 20D, 33A,D, 35H, 47E, 51C, 70F,G, 71C, 71F (modified), 72I, 80D, 89E,F, 90F (modified), 90G, 97E, 99F–H, 101A (modified), 101D, 102B–D; Hiley (1972) 19A, 26A, 27A,B, 27C,D (both modified), 27F, 33B,C (both modified), 33E,F, 71G,H; Leader (1968) 100A–D; Lepneva (1970) 30A,B; Lepneva (1971) 7C, 10C, 72L,N, 76D, 81B, 87F, 90E, 91C,E, 97C,D, 101C,E, 103A; Mackereth (1956) 20C, 21C,D, 22C, 22D (modified), 23A; Murphy (1919) 19E,F; Nielsen (1942) 14I, 20A,B,E,F, 107A; Nielsen (1948) 28B,F,G, 29C,E, 31C, 32A (modified), 32C,G–I (all modified); Siltala (1907) 5A–C, 6D (modified), 28A (modified); Solem (1971) 7H, 103D, 105B–E, 106A,B; Wallace & Wallace (1985) 61C–E, 62D–L; Wallace (1977) 107C–F; Wallace et al. (1985) 76A, 92A,B,D,E, 93A–D,F; Wallace & Wiggins (1977) 102E–H; Wesenburg-Lund (1943) 26B; Wiberg-Larsen (1979) 10E, 12G, 16B,D–H, 17D–F, 18A–G; Wiggins (1977) 28D, 29D, 30C–E, 31A,B,D,E, 32B; Wiggins (1998) 103C. Many other figures come from Hiley (1976) and Wallace (1980, 1981) and we are indebted to the Royal Entomological Society and the publishers of Freshwater Biology for permission to use them here. The figures drawn by Lepneva (listed above) are reproduced by kind permission of Keter Publishing House Jerusalem Ltd, Israel.

Dr D. W. Sutcliffe edited and prepared the key for publication.

REFERENCES

Anderson, N. H. & Bourne, J. R. (1974). Bionomics of three species of glossosomatid caddis flies (Trichoptera: Glossosomatidae) in Oregon. *Can. J. Zool.* **52**, 405–411.

Ashe, P., O'Connor, J. P. & Murray, D. A. (1998). Order Trichoptera. In: A checklist of Irish aquatic insects. *Occasional Publication of the Irish Biogeographical Society* **3**, 27–32.

Badcock, R. M., Bales, M. T. & Harrison, J. D. (1987). Observations on gill number and respiratory adaptation in caddis larvae. *Proceedings 5th Int. Symp. Trichoptera, 1986*, pp. 175–178. Junk, The Hague.

Barnard, P. C. (1971). The larva of *Agraylea sexmaculata* Curtis (Trichoptera, Hydroptilidae). *Entomologist's Gaz.* **22**, 253–257.

Barnard, P. C. (1985). An annotated check-list of the Trichoptera of Britain and Ireland. *Entomologist's Gaz.* **36**, 31–45.

Barnard, P. C. & O'Connor, J. P. (1987). The populations of *Apatania muliebris* McLachlan in the British Isles (Trichoptera: Limnephilidae). *Entomologist's Gaz.* **38**, 263–268.

Botosaneanu, L. (1974). Notes descriptives, faunistiques, écologiques, sur quelques trichoptères du "trio subtroglophile" (Insecta: Trichoptera). *Trav. Inst. Spéol. "Emile Racovitza"*, **13**, 61–75.

Bray, R. P. (1964). *Studies on the British Phryganeidae (Trichoptera) with special reference to the taxonomy and biology of the larvae.* Unpublished Ph.D. Thesis, University of Newcastle upon Tyne.

Bray, R. P. (1966). Records of the Phryganeidae (Trichoptera) in northern England 1961–1964, with a summary of the distribution of British species. *Trans. nat. Hist. Soc. Northumb.* **15**, 226–239.

Bray, R. P. (1967). The taxonomy of the larvae and pupae of the British Phryganeidae (Trichoptera). *J. Zool. Lond.* **153**, 223–244.

Denis, C. (1984). Fine structure of case-making larvae (Trichoptera). In: *Proc. 4th Int. Symp. Trichoptera, 1983*, pp. 105–114. Junk, The Hague.

Disney, R. H. L. (1972). Larval Hydroptilidae (Trichoptera) that prey upon Simuliidae (Diptera) in Cameroon. *Entomologist's mon. Mag.* **108**, 84.

Edington, J. M. & Hildrew, A. G. (1995). A revised key to the caseless caddis larvae of the British Isles with notes on their ecology. *Scient. Publs Freshwat. Biol. Ass.* **53**, 1–134.

Elliott, J. M. (1969). Life history and biology of *Sericostoma personatum* (Spence) (Trichoptera). *Oikos* **20**, 110–118.

Elliott, J. M. (1970). The activity patterns of caddis larvae (Trichoptera). *J. Zool. Lond.* **160**, 279–290.

Elliott, J. M. (1982). A quantitative study of the life cycle of the case-building caddis *Odontocerum albicorne* (Trichoptera: Odontoceridae) in a Lake District stream. *Freshwat. Biol.* **12**, 241–255.

Fahy, E. (1971). The larva of *Hydroptila forcipata* (Eaton) (Trichoptera, Hydroptilidae). *Entomologist's mon. Mag.* **107**, 145–148.

Garside, A. (1979). A character separating the larvae of *Halesus radiatus* (Curtis) and *H. digitatus* (Schrank) (Trichoptera: Limnephilidae). *Entomologist's Gaz.* **30**, 137–139.

Gislason, G. M. (1979). Identification of Icelandic caddis larvae, with descriptions of *Limnephilus fenestratus* (Zett.) and *L. picturatus* McL. (Trichoptera: Limnephilidae, Phryganeidae). *Ent. scand.* **10**, 161–176.

Giudicelli, J. & Vaillant, F. (1967). La larve et la nymphe d'*Allotrichia pallicornis* (Eaton) (Trichoptera). *Trav. Lab. Hydrobiol. Piscic. Univ. Grenoble* **57–58**, 29–36.

Hanna, H. M. (1961). The larva of *Hydroptila sparsa* Curtis (Trichoptera: Hydroptilidae). *Entomologist's Gaz.* **12**, 69–75.

Hetrick, N. D., Morse, J. C. & West, J. L. (1998). Descriptions and phylogeny of four Limnephiloid caddis flies (Trichoptera) based on first instars. *Annals Entomological Society of America* **91**, 497–514.

Hickin, N. E. (1967). *Caddis larvae. Larvae of the British Trichoptera.* Hutchinson, London. xi + 476 pp.

Hiley, P. D. (1972). The taxonomy of the larvae of the British Sericostomatidae (Trichoptera). *Entomologist's Gaz.* **23**, 105–119.

Hiley, P. D. (1973). *The taxonomy of certain caddis-fly larvae, together with an investigation into factors limiting the distribution of selected species.* Unpublished Ph.D. Thesis, University of Newcastle upon Tyne.

Hiley, P. D. (1976). The identification of British limnephilid larvae (Trichoptera). *Syst. Ent.* **1**, 147–167.

Hoffmann, A. (2000). The association of the stream caddisfly *Lasiocephala basalis* (Kol.) (Trichoptera: Lepidostomatidae) with wood. *Int. Revue Hydrobiol.* **85**, 79–93.

Jacquemart, S. (1962). La larve d'*Orthotrichia angustella* McL. (Trichoptère. Hydroptilidae). *Bull. Inst. r. Sci. nat. Belg.* **38** (15), 1–8.

Jacquemart, S. & Coineau, Y. (1962). Missions S. Jacquemart dans les Pyrénées orientals (2e note). Les Trichoptères Hydroptilides des Albères. *Bull. Inst. r. Sci. nat. Belg.* **38** (24), 1–181.

Jenkins, R. A. (1974). Occurrence of *Lasiocephala basalis* (Kolenati) (Trichoptera: Sericostomatidae) in a river in south-west Wales. *Entomologist's mon. Mag.* **110**, 83.

Kachalova, O. L. (1972). *Caddisflies (Trichoptera) of the rivers of Latvia.* Riga. 215 pp.

Kimmins, D. E. (1963). The British species of the genus *Mesophylax*, with further records of the occurrence of *Mesophylax aspersus* (Rambur) in Britain (Trichoptera, Limnephilidae). *Entomologist's Gaz.* **14**, 24–28.

Kimmins, D. E. (1966). A revised checklist of the British Trichoptera. *Entomologist's Gaz.* **17**, 111–120.

Leader, J. P. (1968). The larva of *Molanna palpata* MacLachlan, and some further characters of the larva of *Molanna angustata* Curtis (Trichoptera, Molannidae). *Entomologist's Gaz.* **19**, 21–29.

Lepneva, S. G. (1970). *Fauna of the U.S.S.R. Trichoptera 1, Larvae and pupae of Annulipalpia.* Translation from 1964 Russian edition. Israel Program for Scientific Translations, Jerusalem. iv + 638 pp.

Lepneva, S. G. (1971). *Fauna of the U.S.S.R. Trichoptera 2, Larvae and pupae of Integripalpia.* Translation from 1966 Russian edition. Israel Program for Scientific Translations, Jerusalem. iii + 700 pp.

Macan, T. T. (1973). A key to the adults of the British Trichoptera. *Scient. Publs Freshwat. Biol. Ass.* **28**, 1–151.

MacDonald, W. W. (1950). The larvae of *Mystacides azurea* L., *Cyrnus flavidus* McL. and *Oxyethira simplex* Ris (Trichoptera). *Proc. R. ent. Soc. Lond. (A)* **25**, 19–28.

Mackereth, J. C. (1956). Taxonomy of the larvae of the British species of the sub-family Glossosomatidae (Trichoptera). *Proc. R. ent. Soc. Lond. (A)* **31**, 167– 172.

Marshall, J. E. (1978). Trichoptera: Hydroptilidae. *Handbk Ident. Br. Insects 1*, **14 (a)**, 1–31.

Moretti, G. (1983). *Tricotteri (Trichoptera).* Guide per il riconoscimento delle specie animali delle acque interne Italiene, **19**. Consiglio Nazionale delle Ricerche. Verona. 155 pp.

Morton, K. J. (1890). Notes on the metamorphoses of British Leptoceridae (No. 3). *Entomologist's mon. Mag.* Series 2, **1**, 231–237.

Murphy, H. E. (1919). Observations on the egg-laying of the caddice-fly *Brachycentrus nigrisoma* Banks, and on the habits of the young larvae. *J. N. Y. ent. Soc.* **27**, 154–159.

Nielsen, A. (1942). Uber die Entwicklung und Biologie der Trichopteren mit besonderer Berucksichtigung der Quelltrichopteren Himmerlands. *Arch. Hydrobiol. (Suppl.)* **17**, 255–631.

Nielsen, A. (1948). Postembryonic development and biology of the Hydroptilidae. *Biol. Skr.* **5**, 1–200.

O'Connor, J. P. (1980). *Limnephilus pati* sp. n. (Trichoptera: Limnephilidae), a caddis fly new to Great Britain and Ireland. *Ir. Nat. J.,* **20**, 129–133.

O'Connor, J. P. & Barnard, P. C. (1981). *Limnephilus tauricus* Schmid (Trichoptera: Limnephilidae) new to Great Britain, with a key to the *L. hirsutus* (Pictet) group in the British Isles. *Entomologist's Gaz.* **32**, 115–119.

Panzenbock, W. & Waringer, J. (1997). A key to fifth instar larvae of *Halesus radiatus* Curtis 1834, *Halesus digitatus* Schrank 1781 and *Halesus tesselatus* Rambur 1842 (Trichoptera: Limnephilidae), based on Austrian material. *Aquatic Insects* **19**, 65–73.

Pitsch, T. (1993). Zur larvaltaxonomie, faunistik und okologie mitteleuropaischer liesswasser-kocherfliegen (Insecta: Trichoptera). *Landschaftsentwicklung und Umweltfoschung* **14**, 1–316.

Resh, V. H., Flynn, T. S., Lamberti, G. A., McElravy, E. P., Sorg, K. L. & Wood, J. R. (1981). Responses of the sericostomatid caddis fly *Gumaga nigricula* (McL.) to environmental disruption. In: *Proc. 3rd Int. Symp. Trichoptera, 1980*, pp. 311–318. Junk, The Hague.

Ross, H. H. (1944). The caddisflies, or Trichoptera, of Illinois. *Bull. Ill. St. nat. Hist. Surv.* **23**, 1–326.

Siltala, A. J. (1907). Trichopterologische Untersuchungen. No. 2. Uber die postembryonale Entwicklung der Trichopteren-Larven. *Zool. Jahrb. Suppl.* **9** (2), 309–626, 1 pl.

Snodgrass, R. E. (1935). *Principles of insect morphology.* McGraw-Hill, New York. ix + 667 pp.

Solem, J. O. (1971). Larvae of the Norwegian species of *Phryganea* and *Agrypnia* (Trichoptera, Phryganeidae). *Norsk. ent. Tidsskr.* **18**, 79–88.

Solem, J. O. (1972). The larva of *Agraylea cognatella* McLachlan (Trichoptera, Hydroptilidae). *Norsk. ent. Tidsskr.* **19**, 77–79.

Stroot., P. (1989). The variability of larval colouration patterns of *Agraylea multipunctata* in a population from Belgium (Trichoptera: Hydroptilidae). *Entomologische Berichten Amsterdam* **49**, 157–160.

Wallace, B. & Wallace, I. D. (1985). A key to larvae of the genera *Micropterna* and *Stenophylax* (Trichoptera: Limnephilidae) in Britain and Ireland. *Entomologist's Gaz.* **36**, 127–133.

Wallace, I. D. (1976). *The taxonomy of larvae of the British species of the family Leptoceridae (Trichoptera), with notes on their general biology.* Unpublished Ph.D. Thesis, University of Newcastle upon Tyne.

Wallace, I. D. (1977). A key to larvae and pupae of *Sericostoma personatum* (Spence) and *Notidobia ciliaris* (Linné) (Sericostomatidae: Trichoptera) in Britain. *Freshwat. Biol.* **7**, 93–98.

Wallace, I. D. (1978). On distinguishing the larva of *Limnephilus elegans* Curtis in Britain (Trichoptera: Limnephilidae). *Entomologist's Gaz.* **29**, 177–178.

Wallace, I. D. (1980). The identification of British limnephilid larvae (Trichoptera: Limnephilidae) which have single–filament gills. *Freshwat. Biol.* **10**, 171–189.

Wallace, I. D. (1981). A key to larvae of the family Leptoceridae (Trichoptera) in Great Britain and Ireland. *Freshwat. Biol.* **11**, 273–297.

Wallace, I. D. (1991). A review of the Trichoptera of Great Britain. *Research and Survey in Nature Conservation* **32**, 1–59. Nature Conservancy Council, Peterborough.

Wallace, I. D., Wallace, B. & O'Connor, J. P. (1985). The larva of *Limnephilus fuscinervis* (Trichoptera: Limnephilidae) with notes on the species' distribution and habitat in Ireland. *Ir. Nat. J.* **21**, 397–400.

Wallace, I. D. & Wiggins, G. B. (1978). Observations on the larva and pupa of the caddisfly genus *Hagenella* (Trichoptera: Phryganeidae). In: *Proc. 2nd Int. Symp. Trichoptera, 1977*, pp. 165–173. Junk, The Hague.

Waringer, J. & Graf, W. (1997). *Atlas der Osterreichischen Kocherfliegenlarven unter Einschluss der angrenzenden Gebiete.* Facultas Universitatsverlag, Berggasse, Wien. 286 pp.

Wesenberg-Lund, C. (1943). *Biologie der Susswasserinsekten.* J. Springer, Berlin. 682 pp.

Wiberg-Larsen, P. (1979). Revised key to larvae of Beraeidae in NW Europe (Trichoptera). *Ent. Scand.* **10**, 112–118.

Wichard, W. (1974). Zur morphologischen Anpassung von Tracheenkiemen bei Larven der Limnephilini Kol. (Insecta, Trichoptera). II. Adaptationsversuche unter verschieden O_2 Bedingungen wahrend der larvalen Entwicklung. *Oecologia* **15**, 169–175.

Wiggins, G. B. (1977). *Larvae of the North American caddisfly genera (Trichoptera).* University of Toronto Press, Toronto. 401 pp.

Wiggins, G. B. (1998). *The caddisfly family Phryganeidae (Trichoptera).* University of Toronto, Canada. 306 pp.

INDEX TO FAMILIES, GENERA AND SPECIES

Page numbers in **bold** type indicate illustrations. Redundant names are shown in parentheses.

PUBLICATIONS OF THE FRESHWATER BIOLOGICAL ASSOCIATION

Titles currently available are listed below; further details are given inside the front cover.

FBA SCIENTIFIC PUBLICATIONS

SP 5. Cladocera
A Key to the British Species of Freshwater Cladocera, with Notes on their Ecology, by *D.J. Scourfield & J.P. Harding.*
Third edition, 1966 (reprinted 1994), 61pp. ISBN 0 900386 01 0.

SP 13. Gastropods
A Key to the British Fresh- and Brackish-Water Gastropods, with Notes on their Ecology, by *T. T. Macan.*
Fourth edition, 1977 (reprinted 1994), 46pp. ISBN 0 900386 30 4.

SP 17. Stoneflies
A Key to the Adults and Nymphs of the British Stoneflies (Plecoptera), with Notes on their Ecology and Distribution, by *H.B.N. Hynes.*
Third edition, 1977 (reprinted 1993), 92pp. ISBN 0 900386 28 2.

SP 18. Copepods
A Key to the British Freshwater Cyclopid and Calanoid Copepods, with Ecological Notes, by *J.P. Harding & W.A. Smith.*
Second edition, 1974, 56pp. ISBN 0 900386 20 7.

SP 25. Statistical Analysis
Some Methods for the Statistical Analysis of Samples of Benthic Invertebrates, by *J.M. Elliott.* Second edition, 1977 (reprinted 1993), 160pp. ISBN 0 900386 29 0.

SP 27. Freshwater Fishes
A Key to the Freshwater Fishes of the British Isles, with Notes on their Distribution and Ecology, by *P.S. Maitland.* 1972, 139pp. ISBN 0 900386 18 5.

SP 29. Turbulence
Turbulence in Lakes and Rivers, by *I.R. Smith.*
1975, 79pp. ISBN 0 900386 21 5.

SP 30. Hyphomycetes
An Illustrated Guide to Aquatic and Water-Borne Hyphomycetes (Fungi Imperfecti), with Notes on their Biology, by *C.T. Ingold.*
1975, 96pp. ISBN 0 900386 22 3.

SP 33. Depth Charts
Depth Charts of the Cumbrian Lakes, by *A.E. Ramsbottom.*
1976, 39pp. ISBN 0 900386 25 8.

SP 34. Amoebae
An Illustrated Key to Freshwater and Soil Amoebae, with Notes on Cultivation and Ecology, by *F.C. Page*. 1976, 155pp. ISBN 0 900386 26 6.

SP 36. Water Analysis
Water Analysis: some Revised Methods for Limnologists, by *F.J.H. Mackereth, J. Heron & J.F. Talling*. Second impression, 1989, 120pp. ISBN 0 900386 31 2.

SP 38. Rotifers
A Key to the Freshwater Planktonic and Semi-Planktonic Rotifera of the British Isles, by *R.M. Pontin*. 1978, 178pp. ISBN 0 900386 33 9.

SP 39. Estimating Microbial Numbers
A Guide to Methods for Estimating Microbial Numbers and Biomass in Fresh Water, by *J.G. Jones*. 1979, 112pp. ISBN 0 900386 37 1.

SP 40. Leeches
A Key to the British Freshwater Leeches, with Notes on their Life Cycles and Ecology, by *J.M. Elliott & K.H. Mann*.
1979 (reprinted 1998), 72pp + 1 colour plate. ISBN 0 900386 38 X.

SP 41. Bryozoans
A Key to the British and European Freshwater Bryozoans, by *S.P. Mundy*.
1980, 31pp. ISBN 0 900386 39 8.

SP 42. Desmids
A Key to the Commoner Desmids of the English Lake District, by *E.M. Lind & A.J. Brook*. 1980, 123pp. ISBN 0 900386 40 1.

SP 44. Diatom Frustules
A Guide to the Morphology of the Diatom Frustule, with a Key to the British Freshwater Genera, by *H.G. Barber & E.Y. Haworth*.
1981 (reprinted 1994), 112pp. ISBN 0 900386 42 8.

SP 45. Orthocladiinae Larvae (Chironomidae)
A Key to the Larvae of the British Orthocladiinae (Chironomidae), by *P.S. Cranston*. 1982, 152pp. + 1 plate. ISBN 0 900386 43 6.

SP 46. Parasitic Copepods
The Parasitic Copepoda and Branchiura of British Freshwater Fishes: a Handbook and Key, by *G. Fryer*. 1982, 87pp. ISBN 0 900386 44 4.

SP 47. Adult Mayflies (Ephemeroptera)
A Key to the Adults of the British Ephemeroptera, with Notes on their Ecology, by *J.M. Elliott & U.H. Humpesch*. 1983, 101pp. + 1 plate. ISBN 0 900386 45 2.

SP 48. Mosquitoes (Culicidae)
Keys to the Adults, Male Hypopygia, Fourth-Instar Larvae and Pupae of the British Mosquitoes (Culicidae), with Notes on their Ecology and Medical Importance, by *P.S. Cranston, C.D. Ramsdale, K.R. Snow & G.B. White.* 1987. 152pp. ISBN 0 900386 46 0.

SP 49. Larval Mayflies (Ephemeroptera)
Larvae of the British Ephemeroptera: a Key with Ecological Notes, by *J.M. Elliott, U.H. Humpesch & T.T. Macan.* 1988, 145pp. ISBN 0 900386 47 9.

SP 50. Adult Waterbugs
Adults of the British Aquatic Hemiptera Heteroptera: a Key with Ecological Notes, by *A.A. Savage.* 1989, 173pp. ISBN 0 900386 48 7.

SP 52. Malacostracan Crustaceans
British Freshwater Crustacea Malacostraca: a Key with Ecological Notes, by *T. Gledhill, D.W. Sutcliffe & W.D. Williams.* 1993, 176pp. ISBN 0 900386 53 3.

SP 53. Caseless Caddis Larvae (Trichoptera)
A Revised Key to the Caseless Caddis Larvae of the British Isles, with Notes on their Ecology, by *J.M. Edington & A.G. Hildrew.* 1995, 134pp.ISBN 0 900386 55 X.

SP 54. Alderflies, Lacewings and Spongeflies
British Freshwater Megaloptera and Neuroptera: a Key with Ecological Notes, by *J.M. Elliott.* 1996, 69pp. ISBN 0 900386 56 8.

SP 55. Simuliidae
Last-Instar Larvae and Pupae of the Simuliidae of Britain and Ireland: a Key with Brief Ecological Notes, by *J. Bass.* 1998, 102pp. ISBN 0 900386 58 4.

SP 56. Dixidae and Thaumaleidae
British Dixidae (Meniscus Midges) and Thaumaleidae (Trickle Midges): Keys with Ecological Notes, by *R.H.L. Disney.* 1999, 128pp. ISBN 0 900386 60 6.

SP 57. Larval Corixidae
Keys to the Larvae of British Corixidae, by *A.A. Savage.* 1999, 56pp. ISBN 0 900386 61 4.

SP 58. Triclads
A Key to the Freshwater Triclads of Britain and Ireland, with notes on their ecology, by *T.B. Reynoldson & J.O. Young.* 2000, 72pp. ISBN 0 900386 63 X.

SP 59. Microturbellarians
Keys to the Freshwater Microturbellarians of Britain and Ireland, with notes on their ecology, by *J.O. Young.* 2001, 142pp. ISBN 0 900386 66 5.

SP 60. Coarse Fish Larvae
Keys to Larvae and Juvenile Stages of Coarse Fishes from Fresh Waters in the British Isles, by *A.C. Pinder*. 2001. 136pp. ISBN 0 900386 67 3.

FBA SPECIAL PUBLICATIONS

SPEC 1. A Natural History of the English Lakes
A Natural History of the Lakes, Tarns and Streams of the English Lake District, by *G. Fryer, 1991*. ISBN 0 900386 50 9.
Landscape 184 x 248 mm, sewn and bound between soft covers, 384pp. [Recommended for beginners as a profusely illustrated introduction to freshwater organisms.]

SPEC 3. Eutrophication
Eutrophication: Research and Application to Water Supply, *edited by D.W. Sutcliffe & J.G. Jones, 1992*. ISBN 0 900386 52 5.
Sewn and bound between soft covers, 170 x 245 mm, 224pp.
[The volume contains invited papers from speakers at a specialised conference held in London (UK) on 10–11 December 1991 by the FBA and IWSA. The conference programme combined a balance between theory and its application to management in Belgium, Britain, Denmark, France, Germany, Switzerland and The Netherlands.]

SPEC 4. Water Quality and Stress Indicators
Water Quality and Stress Indicators in Marine and Freshwater Ecosystems: Linking Levels of Organisation (Individuals, Populations, Communities), *edited by D.W. Sutcliffe, 1994*. ISBN 0 900386 54 1.
Sewn and bound between soft covers, 170 x 245 mm, 182pp.
[The volume contains invited papers from speakers and abstracts of poster-presentations at a specialised conference held in Edinburgh on 6–7 September 1993 by the FBA, MBA and SAMS.]

SPEC 5. Microbiological Quality of Water
The Microbiological Quality of Water, *edited by D.W. Sutcliffe, 1997*.
ISBN 0 900386 57 6.
Sewn and bound between soft covers, 170 x 245 mm, 144pp.
[The volume contains invited papers from speakers at a specialised conference held in London (UK) on 12–13 December 1995 by the FBA and IWSA. The conference programme combined a balance between theory and its application to management.]

SPEC 6. English Lakes: Summary and Source Book
Some English Lakes as Diverse and Active Ecosystems: a Factual Summary and Source Book, *compiled and edited by J.F. Talling. 1999*. ISBN 0 900386 59 2.
A5 saddle-stitched between soft covers, 80pp. [The text provides a concise summary of scientific studies on the lakes and tarns of the English Lake District (Cumbria), with 506 numbered references.]

SPEC 7. Aquatic Life Cycle Strategies

Aquatic Life Cycle Strategies: Survival in a Variable Environment, *edited by M. Whitfield, J. Mathews & C. Reynolds, 1999.* ISBN 0 903241 07 2.
Published by the Marine Biological Association of the United Kingdom. Sewn and bound between soft covers, 163 x 240 mm, vii + 149pp. [The volume contains invited papers from speakers at a specialised conference held at the University of Plymouth on 14–17 April 1997 by the FBA, MBA and SAMS.]

SPEC 8. Assessing the Biological Quality of Fresh Waters

Assessing the Biological Quality of Fresh Waters: RIVPACS and Other Techniques, *edited by J.F. Wright, D.W. Sutcliffe & M.T. Furse, 2000.* ISBN 0 900386 62 2.
Sewn and bound, 170 x 250 mm, 400pp.
[This book presents an up-to-date account of developments in predictive bioassessment systems for classifying and monitoring fresh waters, based on macroinvertebrates. It is based on an international workshop of invited scientists from 23 countries that took place in Oxford in 1997.]

SPEC 9. Microbial Diversity in Priest Pot

Microbial Diversity in Priest Pot: a Productive Pond in the English Lake District, *by B.J. Finlay & S.C. Maberly, 2000.* ISBN 0 900386 64 9.
Published in collaboration with the NERC Centre for Ecology and Hydrology, Windermere. Saddle-stiched between soft covers, 174 x 246 mm, 73pp.
[This booklet summarises current knowledge and understanding of the complex interrelationships that exist between micro-organisms and the environment in Priest Pot – a small, shallow pond in the English Lake District which has been studied for more than 50 years.]

SPEC 10. Phytoplankton of Windermere

The Phytoplankton of Windermere (English Lake District), *by C.S. Reynolds & A.E. Irish, 2000.* ISBN 0 900386 65 7.
Published in collaboration with the NERC Centre for Ecology and Hydrology, Windermere. Saddle-stiched between soft covers, 174 x 246 mm, 73pp.
[This booklet provides a factual guide to almost a century's work on the phytoplankton of Windermere – the largest natural lake in England.]

SPEC 11. Windermere

Windermere: Restoring the Health of England's Largest Lake, *by A.D. Pickering, 2001.* ISBN 0 900386 68 1. Sewn and bound between soft covers, 174 x 246 mm, 126 pp, with numerous colour illustrations throughout the text. [Produced to celebrate the 50th Anniversary of the Lake District National Park and the official launch of the Still Waters Partnership of the English Lake District. Written for non-specialist readers, the text covers the postglacial history of the lake, recent major issues of concern that have affected the lake ecosystem, and measures introduced to reverse unwelcome growths of algae and low oxygen concentrations threatening survival of Arctic charr.]